McDougal Littell
Algebra 2

Larson Boswell Kanold Stiff

Chapter 5 Resource Book

The Resource Book contains a wide variety of blackline masters available for Chapter 5. The blacklines are organized by lesson. Included are support materials for the teacher as well as practice, activities, applications, and project resources.

McDougal Littell
A DIVISION OF HOUGHTON MIFFLIN COMPANY
Evanston, Illinois • Boston • Dallas

Contributing Authors

The authors wish to thank the following individuals for their contributions to the Chapter 5 Resource Book.

Karise Mace
Barbara L. Power
Joanne Ricci
Andrew Trapp

ISBN 13: 978-0-618-73449-8
ISBN 10: 0-618-73449-X

6 7 8 9-DSHV-12 11 10 09 08

Contents

Chapter 5 Polynomials and Polynomial Functions

Contents

Contents

Descriptions of Resources

This Chapter Resource Book is organized by lessons within the chapter in order to make your planning easier. The following materials are provided:

Parents as Partners This guide helps parents contribute to student success by providing an overview of the chapter along with questions and activities for parents and students to work on together.

Teaching Guide with Lesson Plan The Teaching Guide provides essential questions, lesson ideas, and classroom strategies to help teachers easily create an engaging class, lead meaningful class discussions and increase the depth of student understanding. A comprehensive list of available resources is provided in the Lesson Plan section to make planning easier.

Investigating Algebra Activities These blackline masters provide extra investigation activities beyond those given in the textbook. These activities help build conceptual understanding before the lesson begins.

Graphing Calculator Activities with Keystrokes Keystrokes for two models of calculators are provided for each Graphing Calculator Activity in the Student Edition, along with alternative Graphing Calculator Activities for selected lessons.

Activity Support Masters These blackline masters make it easier for students to record their work on selected activities in the Student Edition.

Practice A, B, and C These exercises offer additional practice for the material in each lesson, including application problems. There are three levels of practice for each lesson: A (basic), B (average), and C (advanced).

Study Guide These two pages provide additional instruction, worked-out examples, and practice exercises covering the key concepts and vocabulary in each lesson.

Quick Catch-Up for Absent Students This handy form makes it easy for teachers to let students who have been absent know what to do for homework and which activities or examples were covered in class.

Problem Solving Workshops These blackline masters provide extra problem solving opportunities in addition to the workshops given in the textbook. There are three types of workshops: Alternative Methods, Worked-Out Examples, and Mixed Problem Solving.

Interdisciplinary/Real-Life/Math and History Applications Students apply the mathematics covered in each lesson to solve an interesting interdisciplinary, real-life, or historical mathematics problem.

Challenge Practice These exercises offer challenging practice on the mathematics of each lesson.

Chapter Review Games and Activities This worksheet offers fun practice at the end of the chapter and provides an alternative way to review the chapter content in preparation for the Chapter Test.

Project with Rubric The project allows students to delve more deeply into a problem that applies the mathematics of the chapter. Teacher's notes and a 4-point rubric are included.

Cumulative Review These practice pages help students maintain skills from the current chapter and preceding chapters.

**CHAPTER
5** **Parents as Partners**
For use with Chapter 5

Chapter Overview
One way you can help your student succeed in Chapter 5 is by discussing the lesson goals in the chart below. When a lesson is completed, ask your student the following questions. "What were the goals of the lesson? What new words and formulas did you learn? How can you apply the ideas of the lesson to your life?"

Lesson Title	Lesson Goals	Key Applications
5.1: Use Properties of Exponents	Simplify expressions involving powers.	• Locusts • Astronomy • Ocean Volume
5.2: Evaluate and Graph Polynomial Functions	Evaluate and graph other polynomial functions.	• Physical Science • Snowboarding • Diamonds
5.3: Add, Subtract, and Multiply Polynomials	Add, subtract, and multiply polynomials.	• Petroleum • Bicycling • Electronics
5.4: Factor and Solve Polynomial Equations	Factor and solve other polynomial equations.	• City Park • Archaeology • Manufacturing
5.5: Apply the Remainder and Factor Theorems	Use theorems to factor polynomials.	• Business • Clothing • MP3 Players
5.6: Find Rational Zeros	Find all real zeros of a polynomial function.	• Ice Sculptures • Geometry • Swimming Pool
5.7: Apply the Fundamental Theorem of Algebra	Classify the zeros of polynomial functions.	• Tachometer • Physiology • Environment
5.8: Analyze Graphs of Polynomial Functions	Use intercepts to graph polynomial functions.	• Arts and Crafts • Swimming • Post Cards
5.9: Write Polynomial Functions and Models	Write higher-degree polynomial functions.	• Space Exploration • Movie Tickets • Aviation

Big Ideas for Chapter 5

In Chapter 5, you will apply the big ideas listed in the Chapter Opener (see page 329) and reviewed in the Chapter Summary (see page 401).

1. Graphing polynomial functions
2. Performing operations with polynomials
3. Solving polynomial equations and finding zeros

Name _____ Date _____

CHAPTER SUPPORT

CHAPTER 5
Parents as Partners *continued*
For use with Chapter 5

Key Ideas Your student can demonstrate understanding of key concepts by working through the following exercises with you.

Lesson	Exercise
5.1	Simplify $(5x^3y^{-4})^3$. Tell which properties of exponents you used.
5.2	State the degree, type, and leading coefficient of the polynomial function: $g(x) = 6x^3 + 9x^2 - 7$. Then use direct substitution to evaluate the polynomial function for $x = 3$.
5.3	Find the sum, both differences ($a - b$ and $b - a$), and the product of the polynomials $3x^2 - 4x + 9$ and $2x - 5$.
5.4	A storage container is a rectangular prism with a volume of 392 cubic inches. The height of the container is 3 inches less than its length and its width is twice the length. What are the dimensions of the container?
5.5	Divide $2x^2 - 7x + 9$ by $x - 2$.
5.6	A company manufactures metal beams that are used in bridge construction. One piece is a rectangular prism with a height that is 8 times as long as its length and a width of 1 foot greater than its length. The volume of metal used is 16 cubic feet. What are the dimensions of the beam?
5.7	Determine the possible number of positive real zeros, negative real zeros, and imaginary zeros for $f(x) = 5x^3 - 3x^2 - 6$.
5.8	Graph the function: $f(x) = \frac{1}{2}(x + 2)(x - 1)^3$.
5.9	Use finite differences to find a polynomial function that fits the data $(1, 4)$, $(2, 9)$, $(3, 32)$, $(4, 85)$, $(5, 180)$, and $(6, 329)$.

Home Involvement Activity

Directions Find a piece of cardboard of any size. Measure the length and width of the cardboard. Find the dimensions of the box with the smallest volume that you can make from your cardboard. Then find the box with the largest volume.

 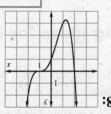

LESSON 5.1 Teaching Guide

Key Concept

You will evaluate numerical expressions and simplify expressions using the properties of exponents.

Teaching the Lesson

Differentiating Instruction: See the Teacher's Edition side column notes on page 331 and the notes on differentiating instruction in the *Algebra 2 Toolkit*.

Teaching Notes and Suggested Questions: See the Teacher's Edition side columns on pages 330–332.

Activity Generator: See the Activity Generator Support Manual.

Animated Algebra: You may want to include the animation on page 331 in your lesson.

See the Teacher's Edition side column notes on page 331

Starting the Lesson

Motivate the Lesson Be sure that students recall the following ideas:

- scientific notation (p. 982)
- evaluating expressions (p. 10)
- evaluating powers (p. 10)

Alternative Lesson Starter

Ancient sword-smiths in Japan followed very specific religious and traditional observances when making Japanese swords. In order for the sword to be both flexible and hard, it was constructed in layers formed by folding and welding metal bars. The process of doubling over the steel was repeated 22 times. This produced 2^{22} or 4,194,302 layers of steel.

Questions to Start the Lesson

1. What is the base of the expression $(-2)^3$? What is the exponent?

2. Evaluate 3^4 and 3^2. Find the product of the results of the two powers. Now, evaluate 3^6.

3. Evaluate 5^2 and 5^3. Find the product of the results of the two powers. Now, evaluate 5^5.

4. What do you notice about the product of two powers with the same base?

5. What is scientific notation? Write the numbers 64,000,000 and 0.00034 in scientific notation.

Common Student Errors

- Forgetting to raise the coefficient to the power when using the *power of a product property*

  Tip Remind students to determine what the base is and raise the entire base by the power.

Example: $(4x^2)^3$

Correct

$4^3 \cdot (x^2)^3 = 64x^6$

Incorrect

$4x^6$

Teaching Strategy of the Day

Motivating Students Start class with a homework review question. Students work using paper and pencil on an exercise similar to the exercises given in the homework assignment. You can walk around the classroom checking to see if the students know how to solve the problem.

LESSON 5.1	**Lesson Plan** *continued*

Standard Schedule: 1 day lesson   Block Schedule: 0.5 day lesson with 5.2

GOAL **Simplify expressions involving powers.**

State Standards _____

Focus and Motivate	**Starting Options**
	_____Homework Check (4.10): TE p. 312; Answer Transparencies
	_____Daily Homework Quiz (4.10): TE p. 315
	_____Warm-Up: TE p. 330 or Transparencies
	_____Starting the Lesson Questions: Teaching Guide
	_____Motivating the Lesson: TE p. 331

Teach	**Teaching Options**
	_____Essential Question: TE p. 330
	_____Alternative Lesson Openers: Electronic Classroom
	_____Classroom Activity: Activity Generator; Chapter Resource Book p. 5
	_____Examples 1–5: PE pp. 330–332
	_____Extra Examples 1–5 with Key Questions: TE pp. 331–332
	_____Real-Life Application: Chapter Resource Book p. 12
	_____Notetaking Guide pp. 132–134

Checking for Understanding
_____Closing the Lesson: TE p. 332
_____Guided Practice Exercises: PE pp. 331–333

Practice and Apply	**Assigning Homework**
	_____Basic: Day 1: SRH p. 982 Exs. 1–4, 21–24; pp. 333–335 Exs. 1–6, 15–17, 25–35 odd, 36–43, 49–52, 56–68 even
	_____Average: Day 1: pp. 333–335 Exs. 1, 2, 7–10, 18–20, 24–34 even, 36–46, 49–53, 56, 59, 62, 65, 68
	_____Advanced: Day 1: pp. 333–335 Exs. 1, 2, 11–14, 21–23, 24–36 even, 40–48*, 50–54*, 57, 60, 63, 66, 69
	_____Block: pp. 333–335 Exs. 1, 2, 7–10, 18–20, 24–34 even, 36–46, 49–53, 56, 59, 62, 65, 68 (with 5.2)
	_____Practice Masters: Chapter Resource Book pp. 6–8 (Levels A, B, or C)

Assess and Reteach	**Differentiating Instruction**
	_____Study Guide: Chapter Resource Book pp. 9–10
	_____Tutorial Software
	_____Challenge: Chapter Resource Book p. 13
	_____Remediation and Intervention Package: _____
	_____English Language Learners Package: _____

Preparing for Standardized Tests
_____Standardized Test Practice: PE pp. 333–335 Exs. 2, 36, 46, 51, 53

Assessing the Lesson
_____Daily Homework Quiz (5.1): TE p. 335 or Transparencies

Name _____ Date _____

 LESSON 5.1

Investigating Algebra Activity: Properties of Exponents

For use before Lesson 5.1

Materials: paper and pencil

QUESTION   **How can you discover the properties of exponents?**

You can discover the properties of exponents by writing exponential functions in expanded form without any exponents. For example, 3^4 can be rewritten in expanded form as $3 \cdot 3 \cdot 3 \cdot 3$.

EXPLORE   **Write exponential expressions in expanded form**

1. Rewrite the exponential expression in expanded form, and then simplify the expression by writing it with an exponent. Several examples have been done.

Property	Exponential expression	Expanded form	Simplified form
Product of powers	$3^5 \cdot 3^2$	$(3 \cdot 3 \cdot 3 \cdot 3 \cdot 3) \cdot (3 \cdot 3)$	3^7
Power of a power	$(2^3)^2$	$(2 \cdot 2 \cdot 2) \cdot (2 \cdot 2 \cdot 2)$	2^6
Quotient of powers	$\dfrac{2^4}{2^2}$	$\dfrac{2 \cdot 2 \cdot 2 \cdot 2}{2 \cdot 2} = 2 \cdot 2$	2^2
Power of a quotient	$\left(\dfrac{2}{5}\right)^3$	$\dfrac{2}{5} \cdot \dfrac{2}{5} \cdot \dfrac{2}{5} = \dfrac{2 \cdot 2 \cdot 2}{5 \cdot 5 \cdot 5}$	$\dfrac{2^3}{5^3}$

  a. Product of powers $6^4 \cdot 6^7$

  b. Power of a power $(3^4)^3$

  c. Quotient of powers $\dfrac{5^8}{5^4}$

  d. Power of a quotient $\left(\dfrac{4}{7}\right)^5$

DRAW CONCLUSIONS   **Use your observations to complete the following.**

2. Compare your answers with a friend. If necessary, use a calculator to verify the correct answer.

3. How do the exponents in the *Exponential expression* column compare to the exponents in the *Simplified form* column for the product of powers property? the power of a power property? the quotient of powers property? the power of a quotient property?

4. Explain what each property means in general.

LESSON 5.1

Name _____ Date _____

Evaluate the power.

1. 3^2 2. 5^3 3. 2^5 4. 4^4

5. 9^0 6. 2^{-1} 7. 7^{-2} 8. 10^{-6}

Evaluate the expression. Tell which properties of exponents you used.

9. $4^2 \cdot 4^3$ 10. $(-3)^4(-3)$ 11. $(5^2)^3$

12. $(7^0)^5$ 13. $2^0 \cdot 2^{-5}$ 14. $\dfrac{3^7}{3^4}$

15. $(10^3)^3$ 16. $\left(\dfrac{5}{6}\right)^2$ 17. $\dfrac{(-5)^6}{-5}$

18. $\dfrac{8^2}{8^3}$ 19. $\dfrac{9^2}{9^{-2}}$ 20. $\left(\dfrac{1}{2}\right)^{-5}$

Write the number in scientific notation.

21. 527,000   22. 0.0000526

23. 0.0023   24. 5,983,000,000,000

25. 17,600,000,000,000,000   26. 0.0000007

Write the answer in scientific notation.

27. $(3.2 \times 10^4)(1.5 \times 10^5)$ 28. $(5.7 \times 10^{-6})(6.2 \times 10^8)$

29. $(2.8 \times 10^3)^2$ 30. $(4.3 \times 10^2)^2$

31. $\dfrac{8.4 \times 10^{10}}{1.4 \times 10^8}$ 32. $\dfrac{3.6 \times 10^{-5}}{4.8 \times 10^{-7}}$

Simplify the expression. Tell which properties of exponents you used.

33. $b^4 \cdot b^2$ 34. $x^{-3} \cdot x^5$

35. $(s^7)^2$ 36. $(5y)^2$

37. $\dfrac{z^9}{z^5}$ 38. $\dfrac{m^2}{m^6}$

39. $\left(\dfrac{x}{3}\right)^3$ 40. $\left(\dfrac{n}{4}\right)^{-2}$

41. **Earth Science** The total volume of water on Earth is about 326,000,000 cubic miles. Write this number in scientific notation.

42. **National Debt** On August 1, 2005, the national debt of the United States was about $7,870,000,000,000. The population of the United States at that time was about 297,000,000. If the national debt was divided evenly among everyone in the country, how much would each person owe? Write your answer in scientific notation.

Name _____ Date _____

Practice B

For use with pages 330–335

Evaluate the expression. Tell which properties of exponents you used.

1. $2^5 \cdot 2^3$

2. $(-7)^2(-7)$

3. $4^{-6} \cdot 4^{-1}$

4. $(5^{-2})^2$

5. $\dfrac{4^{-7}}{4^{-3}}$

6. $\dfrac{8^{-4}}{8^2}$

7. $\left(\dfrac{2}{3}\right)^3$

8. $\left(\dfrac{4}{5}\right)^{-3}$

Write the answer in scientific notation.

9. $(6.1 \times 10^5)(2.2 \times 10^6)$

10. $(2.6 \times 10^{-7})(1.3 \times 10^2)$

11. $(3.4 \times 10^{-1})(3.1 \times 10^{-2})$

12. $(5.8 \times 10^{-7})(8.1 \times 10^{12})$

13. $(4.5 \times 10^4)^2$

14. $(3.7 \times 10^{-5})^2$

15. $(7.2 \times 10^{-3})^3$

16. $\dfrac{9.9 \times 10^9}{1.5 \times 10^8}$

17. $\dfrac{8.4 \times 10^{-6}}{2.4 \times 10^9}$

Simplify the expression. Tell which properties of exponents you used.

18. $\dfrac{x^8}{x^4}$

19. $\dfrac{y^4}{y^{-7}}$

20. $(3^2 s^3)^6$

21. $(4^0 w^2)^{-5}$

22. $(y^4 z^2)(y^{-3} z^{-5})$

23. $(2m^3 n^{-1})(8m^4 n^{-2})$

24. $(7c^7 d^2)^{-2}$

25. $(5g^4 h^{-3})^{-3}$

26. $\dfrac{x^5 y^{-8}}{x^5 y^{-6}}$

27. $\dfrac{16q^0 r^{-6}}{4q^{-3} r^{-7}}$

28. $\dfrac{12a^{-3} b^9}{21a^2 b^{-5}}$

29. $\dfrac{8e^{-4} f^{-2}}{18ef^{-5}}$

Write an expression for the surface area or volume in terms of x.

30. $S = 4\pi r^2$

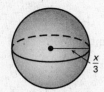

31. $V = \dfrac{1}{3}\pi r^2 h$

32. $V = \dfrac{4}{3}\pi r^3$

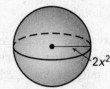

33. **Birds** Some scientists estimate that there are about 8600 species of birds in the world. The mean number of birds per species is approximately 12,000,000. About how many birds are there in the world? Write your answer in scientific notation.

34. **Biology** A red blood cell has a diameter of approximately 0.00075 centimeter. If one of the arteries in your body has a diameter of 0.0456 centimeter, how many red blood cells could fit across the artery? Write your answer in scientific notation.

LESSON 5.1 **Practice C**
For use with pages 330–335

Evaluate the expression. Tell which properties of exponents you used.

1. $5^0 \cdot 5^5 \cdot 5^{-3}$

2. $\dfrac{3^{-2} \cdot 3^4}{3^{-5}}$

3. $\dfrac{(2^3)^2}{2^{-4}}$

4. $\dfrac{(-4)^2(-4)^{-3}}{(-4)^{-5}}$

5. $\left(\dfrac{3}{4}\right)^{-3}$

6. $\left(\left(\dfrac{1}{3}\right)^{-2}\right)^3$

7. $\dfrac{\left(\dfrac{2}{3}\right)^4}{\left(\dfrac{2}{3}\right)^{-5}\left(\dfrac{2}{3}\right)^0}$

8. $\dfrac{\left(\dfrac{1}{5}\right)^{-4}}{\left(\dfrac{1}{5}\right)^{-2}\left(\dfrac{1}{5}\right)^{-5}}$

Write the answer in scientific notation.

9. $(2.3 \times 10^{-4})(9.3 \times 10^8)$

10. $(5.4 \times 10^{-5})(1.8 \times 10^{-1})$

11. $(2.5 \times 10^{-3})^{-2}$

12. $\dfrac{(3.3 \times 10^9)(2.8 \times 10^{-7})}{4.62 \times 10^5}$

13. $\dfrac{(1.2 \times 10^{-4})^2}{(9.0 \times 10^5)(1.6 \times 10^{-8})}$

14. $\dfrac{2.1 \times 10^{-4}}{8.4 \times 10^{-6}}$

Simplify the expression. Tell which properties of exponents you used.

15. $\dfrac{x^2 y^3}{2} \cdot \dfrac{2x^4}{y^3}$

16. $\dfrac{4m^4}{-6m^{-1}n^5} \cdot \dfrac{3n^{-1}}{m^{-2}}$

17. $\dfrac{(c^4)^3}{4} \cdot \dfrac{12d^{-6}}{(15cd)^{-1}}$

18. $\dfrac{w^{-3}}{v^{-5}} \cdot \dfrac{v^{-5}}{w^{-3}}$

19. $\left(\dfrac{x^7 y^{-2}}{3y^{-3}}\right)^{-2}$

20. $\left(\dfrac{qr^2 s}{3r^4}\right)^{-3}$

21. $[(z^{-2})^2]^3$

22. $[(b^9)^{-1}]^{-2}$

Write an expression that makes the statement true.

23. $a^4 b^{-3} c^5 \cdot \underline{\ ?\ } = a^8 bc^{10}$

24. $\dfrac{?}{9x^2 y^6 z} = \dfrac{2x}{3y^2}$

25. $(2m^3 n^2)^6 = \underline{\ ?\ } \cdot 4m^{12}n^{-5}$

26. Chemistry One milliliter of water contains about 3.33×10^{22} molecules. About how many molecules are in a 0.5 liter bottle of water? Write your answer in scientific notation.

27. Manufacturing A package designer for a company that makes holiday ornaments needs to decide how to package a special edition glass ornament shaped like a sphere. It must be packaged as tightly as possible in a cylinder or a cube.

  a. Write an expression for the ratio of the volume of the ornament to the volume of the cylinder.

  b. Write an expression for the ratio of the volume of the ornament to the volume of the cube.

  c. Which package do you think the designer should choose? *Explain.*

LESSON 5.1 Study Guide
For use with pages 330–335

GOAL Simplify expressions involving powers.

> **Vocabulary**
>
> A number is expressed in **scientific notation** if it is in the form $c \times 10^n$ where $1 \le c < 10$ and n is an integer.

EXAMPLE 1 **Evaluate a numerical expression**

$$\left(\frac{1}{3^{-2}}\right)^3 (-4)^3 = (3^2)^3 (-4)^3 \qquad \text{Negative exponent property}$$

$$= 3^6 (-4)^3 \qquad \text{Power of a power property}$$

$$= 729(-64) = -46{,}656 \qquad \text{Evaluate power.}$$

EXAMPLE 2 **Use scientific notation in real life**

Hoover Dam The volume of concrete that was used to construct the Hoover Dam is about 3,325,000 cubic yards. One cubic yard of concrete weighs about 4050 pounds. About how many pounds of concrete were used to construct the Hoover Dam?

Solution

$$\boxed{\begin{array}{c}\text{Pounds of}\\\text{concrete}\end{array}} = \boxed{\begin{array}{c}\text{Weight per}\\\text{cubic yard}\end{array}} \times \boxed{\begin{array}{c}\text{Number of}\\\text{cubic yards}\end{array}}$$

$$= \quad 4050 \quad \times \quad 3{,}325{,}000 \qquad \text{Substitute values.}$$

$$= (4.05 \times 10^3)(3.325 \times 10^6) \qquad \text{Write in scientific notation.}$$

$$= (4.05 \times 3.325)(10^3 \times 10^6) \qquad \text{Use multiplication properties.}$$

$$= 13.46625 \times 10^9 \qquad \text{Product of powers property}$$

$$= 1.346625 \times 10^1 \times 10^9 \qquad \text{Write 13.46625 in scientific notation.}$$

$$= 1.346625 \times 10^{10} \qquad \text{Product of powers property}$$

The number of pounds of concrete is about 1.346625×10^{10}, or about 13,466,250,000 pounds.

Exercises for Examples 1 and 2

Evaluate the expression. Tell which properties of exponents you used.

1. $(2^2 \cdot 5)^3$ **2.** $7^3 \cdot 7^{-1}$ **3.** $(8^0 \cdot 6^{-2})^{-1}$ **4.** $\left(\frac{9^6}{9^4}\right)^3$

5. Rework Example 2 for the Shasta Dam that contains 6.3 million cubic yards of concrete.

LESSON 5.1 Study Guide *continued*
For use with pages 330–335

EXAMPLE 3 Simplify an expression

Simplify the expression. Tell which properties of exponents you used.

$$\frac{y^7z^4}{(z^{-2})^{-1}z^2} = \frac{y^7z^4}{z^2z^2} \qquad \text{Power of a power property}$$

$$= \frac{y^7z^4}{z^4} \qquad \text{Product of powers property}$$

$$= y^7z^0 \qquad \text{Quotient of powers property}$$

$$= y^7 \cdot 1 \qquad \text{Zero exponent property}$$

$$= y^7 \qquad \text{Identity property of multiplication}$$

EXAMPLE 4 Compare real-life volumes

Softball The radius of a softball is about $\frac{4}{3}$ times the radius of a baseball. How many times as great as the baseball's volume is the softball's volume?

Solution

Let r represent the radius of a baseball. Then $\frac{4}{3}r$ represents the radius of a softball.

$$\frac{\text{softball's volume}}{\text{baseball's volume}} = \frac{\frac{4}{3}\pi\left(\frac{4}{3}r\right)^3}{\frac{4}{3}\pi r^3} \qquad \text{The volume of a sphere is } \frac{4}{3}\pi r^3.$$

$$= \frac{\frac{4}{3}\pi\left(\frac{4}{3}\right)^3 r^3}{\frac{4}{3}\pi r^3} \qquad \text{Power of a product property}$$

$$= \frac{64}{27}r^0 \qquad \text{Power of a quotient and quotient of powers}$$

$$= \frac{64}{27} \cdot 1 \qquad \text{Zero exponent property}$$

$$\approx 2.370370 \qquad \text{Use a calculator.}$$

The volume of a softball is about 2.37 times as great as the volume of a baseball.

Exercises for Examples 3 and 4

Simplify the expression. Tell which properties of exponents you used.

6. $t^7t^2t^{-8}$ **7.** $(k^{-3}m^4)^{-2}$ **8.** $\left(\frac{f^5}{g^{-2}}\right)^{-3}$ **9.** $\left(\frac{3x}{z^2}\right)^0$

10. Rework Example 4 where the radius of a volleyball is about 3 times the radius of a baseball.

Quick Catch-Up for Absent Students

LESSON 5.1

For use with pages 330–335

The items checked below were covered in class on (date missed) _____

Lesson 5.1: Use Properties of Exponents

_____ **Goal:** Simplify expressions involving powers. (pp. 330–333)

Material Covered:

_____ Avoid errors

_____ Example 1: Evaluate numerical expressions

_____ Example 2: Use scientific notation in real life

_____ Review scientific notation

_____ Guided Practice for Examples 1 and 2

_____ Example 3: Simplifying expressions

_____ Interpret bases

_____ Example 4: Standardized Test Practice

_____ Example 5: Compare real-life volumes

_____ Guided Practice for Examples 3, 4, and 5

Vocabulary:

scientific notation, p. 331

_____ Other (specify)

_____

Homework and Additional Learning Support

_____ Textbook (specify) pp. 333–335

_____

_____ *Study Guide* worksheet (specify exercises)_____

_____ *@HomeTutor* for Lesson 5.1

LESSON 5.1 Real-Life Application: When Will I Ever Use This?

For use with pages 330–335

LESSON 5.1

Planetary Motion

Johannes Kepler (1571–1630) discovered that the orbits of planets in our solar system follow paths around the sun that are ellipses. Kepler discovered several laws about planetary motion, one of which is described below.

In Exercises 1–6, use the following information.

In 1619, Kepler discovered that the period P (in years, where one year is 365.25 days) of each planet in our solar system is related to the planet's mean distance a (in astronomical units) from the sun by the equation $\dfrac{P^2}{a^3} = k$. This relationship is often referred to as Kepler's third law of planetary motion.

1. One astronomical unit is approximately (a) 149,600,000 kilometers or (b) 93,000,000 miles. Write both numbers using scientific notation.

2. Test Kepler's equation for the nine planets in our solar system using the table below. (Astronomical units relate the other planets' periods and mean distances to Earth's period and mean distance.) Is k approximately the same value for each planet?

Planet	P	a
Mercury	0.241	0.387
Venus	0.615	0.723
Earth	1.000	1.000
Mars	1.881	1.523
Jupiter	11.861	5.203
Saturn	29.457	9.541
Uranus	84.008	19.190
Neptune	164.784	30.086
Pluto	248.350	39.507

3. When looking through your telescope you discover a planet whose mean distance from the sun is 48.125 astronomical units. Use the results in Exercise 2 to find the period of this planet in days. (The period of Earth is 365.25 days.)

4. Find the ratio of Pluto's mean distance from the sun to Mercury's mean distance.

5. You are drawing a diagram of our solar system in which Mercury's mean distance from the sun is represented by 1 inch. How many inches will be needed to represent Pluto's mean distance from the sun?

6. Redo the table given in Exercise 2 using scientific notation.

LESSON 5.1 Challenge Practice

For use with pages 330–335

In Exercises 1–4, simplify the expression, where *n* is an integer.

1. $(x^n y^{2n})^n$

2. $x^{2n} \cdot x + y^{-n} \cdot y^2$

3. $\left(\dfrac{x^n x^2}{y^{3n} y}\right)^{-2}$

4. $\left(\dfrac{x^0 x^{-n} y^3}{x^4 y^n y^{-1}}\right)^{-1}$

In Exercises 5–8, decide whether the expression is *positive* or *negative*, given that *a* < 0 and *b* > 1.

5. $(a^{-1} b^0)^3$

6. $(a^5 b^{-1})^0$

7. $a^{-1} + b$

8. $a^0 b^2 - b$

9. Prove the power of a power property of exponents, $(a^m)^n = a^{mn}$, for each condition.

   a. *m* is a positive integer and *n* is a negative integer.

   b. *m* is a negative integer and *n* is a positive integer.

   c. *m* and *n* are negative integers.

   d. *m* is a positive integer and *n* is 0.

10. **Escape Velocity** The *escape velocity* for a projectile is the velocity required for the projectile to escape from a massive central body to a point at infinity. The following equation can be used to model escape velocity.

    $$\frac{1}{2} m v^2 = \frac{GMm}{r}$$

    In the model, *v* is the escape velocity, *m* is the mass of the projectile, *G* is the universal gravitational constant, *M* is the mass of the central body, and *r* is radius of the central body. The initial velocity of the projectile must reach or exceed the escape velocity in order for the projectile to travel infinitely into space.

    a. Solve the given equation for *v*.

    b. A rocket weighing 200,000 kilograms is launched vertically from Earth at an initial velocity of 10,000 meters per second. Determine the rocket's escape velocity if the mass of Earth is 5.97×10^{24} kilograms, the radius of Earth is 6378 kilometers, and the universal gravitational constant is given by 6.67×10^{-11} cubic meters per kilogram-second squared. Will the rocket travel infinitely into space?

    c. Using your results from parts (a) and (b), what is the escape velocity for any projectile launched from Earth? *Explain* your reasoning.

LESSON 5.2 Teaching Guide

Key Concept

You will identify polynomial functions by the degree of the polynomial. You will evaluate polynomial functions using either direct substitution or synthetic substitution. You will use the end behavior of the function and a table of values to graph polynomial functions.

Teaching the Lesson

Differentiating Instruction: See the Teacher's Edition side column notes on pages 338 and 339 and the notes on differentiating instruction in the *Algebra 2 Toolkit*.

Teaching Notes and Suggested Questions: See the Teacher's Edition side columns on pages 337–340.

Activity Generator: See the Activity Generator Support Manual.

Animated Algebra: You may want to include the animation on page 340 in your lesson.

Starting the Lesson

Connect to Prior Learning Be sure that students recall the following ideas:

- graph quadratic functions in standard form (p. 236)

- graph quadratic functions in vertex or intercept form (p. 245)

- domain and range (p. 72)

Alternative Lesson Starter

Ruth Bari's use of chromatic polynomials helps mapmakers determine the number of ways to best color a map, without the same colors touching, based on the number of colors available.

Questions to Start the Lesson

1. What is the standard form of a quadratic equation? What do we mean when we say a function is in standard form?

2. What is the degree of a linear equation? How many turning points does a linear function have? What is the degree of a quadratic function? How many turning points does this type of graph have? How does this concept help you choose x-values when making a table of values to graph?

3. What do you think will happen to a graph as the degree of a polynomial function increases? How can restricting the domain of a graph and examining the interval defined by that domain help you understand a graph's behavior? Why is this important?

Common Student Errors

- Forgetting to write zeros for the missing terms of a polynomial when using synthetic substitution

  Tip Have students write the polynomial in standard form and fill in missing terms with zero coefficients. Then use the coefficient of each term to perform the synthetic substitution.

Example: $3x^2 + 2x^3 - 7$

In standard form with the missing term:

$2x^3 + 3x^2 + 0x - 7$

Teaching Strategy of the Day

Asking Questions Limit questions that rely on memory. Students may recite the answer, but this will not tell you if they understand the lesson goals.

LESSON 5.2	**Lesson Plan** *continued*

Standard Schedule: 2 day lesson   Block Schedule: 0.5 day lesson with 5.1, and 0.5 day with 5.3

GOAL **Evaluate and graph other polynomial functions.**

State Standards _____

Focus and Motivate

Starting Options
_____ Homework Check (5.1): TE p. 333; Answer Transparencies
_____ Daily Homework Quiz (5.1): TE p. 335
_____ Warm-Up: TE p. 337 or Transparencies
_____ Starting the Lesson Questions: Teaching Guide
_____ Motivating the Lesson: TE p. 338

Teach

Teaching Options
_____ Essential Question: TE p. 337
_____ Alternative Lesson Openers: Electronic Classroom
_____ Classroom Activity: Activity Generator; Chapter Resource Book p. 16
_____ Examples 1–6: PE pp. 337–340
_____ Extra Examples 1–6 with Key Questions: TE pp. 338–340
_____ Problem Solving Workshop: Worked Out Example: Chapter Resource Book p. 24
_____ Notetaking Guide pp. 135–137

Checking for Understanding
_____ Closing the Lesson: TE p. 340
_____ Guided Practice Exercises: PE pp. 338–341

Practice and Apply

Assigning Homework
_____ Basic: Day 1: pp. 341–344 Exs. 1–5, 9–12, 15–23 odd, 61–72;
Day 2: pp. 341–344 Exs. 24–32, 37–43, 54–58, 73–78
_____ Average: Day 1: pp. 341–344 Exs. 1, 2, 5–7, 10–13, 16–22 even, 23, 61–72;
Day 2: pp. 341–344 Exs. 24–27, 30–34, 37, 43–46, 50, 54–59, 73–78
_____ Advanced: Day 1: pp. 341–344 Exs. 1, 2, 6–8, 11–14, 18–22, 61–72;
Day 2: pp. 341–344 Exs. 24–26, 34–37, 44–53*, 56–60*, 73–78
_____ Block: pp. 341–344 Exs. 1, 2, 5–7, 10–13, 16–22 even, 23, 61–72
(with 5.1); pp. 341–344 Exs. 24–27, 30–34, 37, 43–46, 50, 54–59, 73–78 (with 5.3)
_____ Practice Masters: Chapter Resource Book pp. 18–20 (Levels A, B, or C)

Assess and Reteach

Differentiating Instruction
_____ Study Guide: Chapter Resource Book pp. 21–22
_____ Tutorial Software
_____ Challenge: Chapter Resource Book p. 25
_____ Remediation and Intervention Package: _____
_____ English Language Learners Package: _____

Preparing for Standardized Tests
_____ Standardized Test Practice: PE pp. 341–344 Exs. 2, 24, 37, 50, 52, 59

Assessing the Lesson
_____ Daily Homework Quiz (5.2): TE p. 344 or Transparencies

LESSON 5.2

LESSON 5.2 Graphing Calculator Keystrokes

For use with Investigating Algebra Activity 5.2 on page 336

TI-83 Plus

STEP 1

a. Y= | X,T,θ,n | ^ | 4 | ZOOM | 6

b. Y= | (−) | X,T,θ,n | ^ | 4 | ZOOM | 6

Casio CFX-9850GC Plus

STEP 1

a. From the main menu, choose GRAPH.

X,θ,T | ^ | 4 | EXE | SHIFT | F3 | F3 | EXIT | F6

b. From the main menu, choose GRAPH.

(−) | X,θ,T | ^ | 4 | EXE | SHIFT | F3 | F3 | EXIT | F6

Graphing Calculator Keystrokes

LESSON 5.2

For use with Graphing Calculator Activity 5.2 on page 345

TI-83 Plus

STEP 1

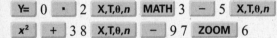

Y= | 0 | · | 2 | X,T,θ,n | MATH | 3 | − | 5 | X,T,θ,n

x² | + | 3 8 | X,T,θ,n | − | 9 7 | ZOOM | 6

STEP 2

WINDOW | ENTER | 2 0 | GRAPH

STEP 3

WINDOW | ENTER | ENTER | ENTER

(−) | 2 0 | GRAPH

Casio CFX-9850GC Plus

STEP 1

From the main menu, choose GRAPH.

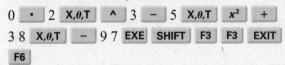

0 | · | 2 | X,θ,T | ^ | 3 | − | 5 | X,θ,T | x² | +

3 8 | X,θ,T | − | 9 7 | EXE | SHIFT | F3 | F3 | EXIT

F6

STEP 2

SHIFT | F3 | ▼ | 2 0 | EXE | EXIT | F6

STEP 3

SHIFT | F3 | ▼ | ▼ | ▼ | (−) | 2 0 | EXE | EXIT

F6

LESSON 5.2 **Practice A**
For use with pages 336–345

Decide whether the function is a polynomial function. If it is, write the function in standard form.

1. $f(x) = 5x + 2$

2. $f(x) = 2^x$

3. $g(x) = 15 + 3x^2 + x$

4. $h(x) = \frac{1}{2}x^4 - x^2 + 3x^3$

State the degree, type, and leading coefficient of the polynomial.

5. $g(x) = 2x^2 - 4x + 9$

6. $h(x) = 7 - 3x$

7. $f(x) = -\frac{3}{4}x^3 + 2x^4 + 7$

8. $g(x) = 8x - 6 + x^3\sqrt{2}$

Use direct substitution to evaluate the polynomial function for the given value of *x*.

9. $f(x) = 3x^3 + 4x^2 - 5x + 7; x = 1$

10. $g(x) = x^5 - 2x + 3x^2 - 9; x = 2$

11. $h(x) = 4x - 8x^6 + 1; x = 0$

12. $f(x) = x + 2x^3 - x^4 - 10; x = -2$

Use synthetic substitution to evaluate the polynomial function for the given value of *x*.

13. $g(x) = 2x^3 - 5x^2 + 4x - 1; x = 1$

14. $h(x) = x^4 + 7x^3 + x^2 - 2x - 6; x = -3$

Use what you know about end behavior to match the polynomial function with its graph.

15. $f(x) = 2x^4 + 2x - 1$

16. $f(x) = -x^2 + 3x - 2$

17. $f(x) = 2x^3 + x^2 - 1$

A.

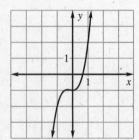

B.

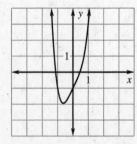

C.

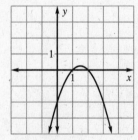

18. Business The cost of manufacturing a certain product can be modeled by the function $C(n) = 0.2n^3 - 7n^2 + 108n + 100$ where *C* is the cost in dollars and *n* is the number of units of the product in thousands.

a. State the degree and type of the function.

b. Complete the table of values for the function.

n	0	5	10	15	20
C					

c. Use your table to graph the function.

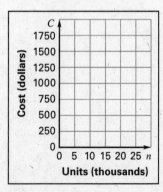

Algebra 2

LESSON 5.2 **Practice B**
For use with pages 336–345

Decide whether the function is a polynomial function. If it is, write the function in standard form and state the degree, type, and leading coefficient.

1. $f(x) = 7 - 2x$

2. $g(x) = 2x - x^3 + 8$

3. $h(x) = x^4 - x^{-3}$

Use direct substitution to evaluate the polynomial function for the given value of x.

4. $f(x) = 6x^4 - x^3 + 3x^2 - 5x + 9; x = -1$

5. $g(x) = 7x - x^4 + 1; x = -4$

Use synthetic substitution to evaluate the polynomial function for the given value of x.

6. $f(x) = 7x^4 - 3x^3 + x^2 + 5x - 9; x = 2$

7. $g(x) = x^3 - 8x + 6; x = -3$

Describe the end behavior of the graph of the polynomial function by completing these statements: $f(x) \rightarrow \underline{\ ?\ }$ as $x \rightarrow -\infty$ and $f(x) \rightarrow \underline{\ ?\ }$ as $x \rightarrow +\infty$.

8. $f(x) = -5x^3$

9. $f(x) = 2x^5 - 7x^2 - 4x$

10. $f(x) = 2x^8 + 9x^7 + 10$

11. $f(x) = -12x^6 - 2x + 5$

Graph the polynomial function.

12. $f(x) = -x^3 - 2$

13. $g(x) = x^4 + 2x$

14. $h(x) = -x^4 + 2x^3 - 5x + 1$

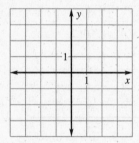
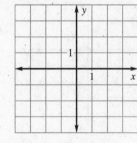
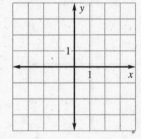

15. **Shopping** The retail space in shopping centers in the United States from 1986 to 2003 can be modeled by

$S = -0.0388t^4 + 1.723t^3 - 28t^2 + 309t + 3481$

where S is the amount of retail space (in millions of square feet) and t is the number of years since 1986.

a. Describe the end behavior of the graph of the function.

b. Graph the function on the domain $0 \le t \le 17$.

c. Use the graph to estimate the first year that the amount of retail space was greater than 5000 million square feet.

d. Use the model to predict the amount of retail space in the year 2010. Is it appropriate to use the model to make this prediction? *Explain.*

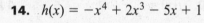

LESSON 5.2

Practice C
For use with pages 336–345

Decide whether the function is a polynomial function. If it is, write the function in standard form and state the degree, type, and leading coefficient.

1. $f(x) = x^3\sqrt{5} + 7 - 2x^2$

2. $g(x) = \pi - 4x^2 + \dfrac{2}{x}$

Use direct substitution to evaluate the polynomial function for the given value of *x*. Then check your answer using synthetic substitution.

3. $f(x) = 2x^5 - 3x^4 + x^3 - 6x + 20; x = 2$

4. $g(x) = -8x^3 + 5x^2 + 14; x = -3$

5. Critical Thinking Give an example of a polynomial function that is easier to evaluate using direct substitution rather than synthetic substitution. *Explain.*

Describe the end behavior of the graph of the polynomial function by completing these statements: $f(x) \to$ __?__ **as** $x \to -\infty$ **and** $f(x) \to$ __?__ **as** $x \to +\infty$.

6. $f(x) = -x^7 + 10x$

7. $f(x) = 0.6x^3 - 2x^2 + 27$

8. $f(x) = x^{102} + 4x^{99}$

9. $f(x) = -x^{250} + 100x^{200}$

Graph the polynomial function.

10. $f(x) = \dfrac{1}{2} - 2x^4$

11. $g(x) = -2x^7 - 4$

12. $h(x) = x^3\sqrt{2} - 2x + 3$

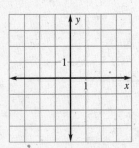
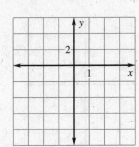
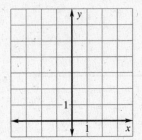

13. Critical Thinking Give an example of a polynomial function f such that $f(x) \to -\infty$ as $x \to -\infty$ and $f(x) \to -\infty$ as $x \to +\infty$.

14. Child Development The average height (in inches) for boys B and girls G ages 2 to 20 can be modeled by the functions
$B = -0.001t^4 + 0.04t^3 - 0.57t^2 + 5.7t + 25$ and
$G = 0.000007t^4 - 0.00276t^3 - 0.012t^2 + 3.1t + 27$
where t is the age (in years).

a. According to the models, what is the difference in average height between 16-year-old boys and girls?

b. Sketch the graphs of the two models in the same coordinate plane.

c. During an annual physical, a doctor measures a 14-year-old to be 60 inches tall. Is the 14-year-old more likely to be male or female? *Explain.*

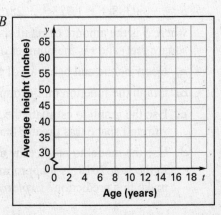

Algebra 2
Chapter 5 Resource Book

Study Guide

LESSON 5.2
For use with pages 336–345

GOAL Evaluate and graph other polynomial functions.

Vocabulary

A **polynomial** is monomial or a sum of monomials.

A **polynomial function** is a function of the form

$f(x) = a_n x^n + a_{n-1} x^{n-1} + \cdots + a_1 x + a_0$ where $a^n \neq 0$, the exponents are all whole numbers, and the coefficients are all real numbers.

Synthetic substitution is another way to evaluate a polynomial function, involving fewer operations than direct substitution.

The **end behavior** of a polynomial function's graph is the behavior of the graph as x approaches positive infinity or negative infinity.

EXAMPLE 1 ## Identify polynomial functions

Decide whether the function is a polynomial function. If so, write it in standard form and state its degree, type, and leading coefficient.

a. $g(x) = -5x + 6x^{-2}$

b. $t(x) = -\sqrt{5}x + 2$

Solution

a. The function $g(x)$ is not a polynomial function because the term $6x^{-2}$ has an exponent that is not a whole number.

b. The function $t(x)$ is a polynomial function written in standard form. It has degree 1 (linear) and a leading coefficient of $-\sqrt{5}$.

EXAMPLE 2 ## Evaluate a polynomial function

Use (a) direct substitution and (b) synthetic substitution to evaluate $g(x) = -4x^3 + 3x^2 - 7$ when $x = -2$.

Solution

a. $g(x) = -4x^3 + 3x^2 - 7$ Write original function.

  $g(-2) = -4(-2)^3 + 3(-2)^2 - 7$ Substitute -2 for x.

  $= 37$ Simplify.

b.

STEP 1 Write the coefficients of $f(x)$ in order of descending exponents. Write the value a which $f(x)$ is being evaluated to the left.

$$-2 \begin{array}{|rrrr} -4 & 3 & 0 & -7 \end{array}$$

LESSON 5.2

Study Guide *continued*
For use with pages 336–345

STEP 2 **Bring** down the leading coefficient. Multiply
the leading coefficient by the *x*-value. Write
the product under the second coefficient. Add.

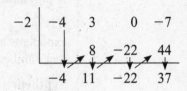

STEP 3 **Multiply** the previous sum by the *x*-value.
Write the product under the second coefficient.
Add. Repeat for all the remaining coefficients.
The final sum is the value of $f(x)$ at the given
x-value.

$$\begin{array}{c|cccc} -2 & -4 & 3 & 0 & -7 \\ & & 8 & -22 & 44 \\ \hline & -4 & 11 & -22 & 37 \end{array}$$

Synthetic substitution gives $g(x) = 37$, which matches the result in part (a).

Exercises for Examples 1 and 2

**If the function is a polynomial function, write it in standard form and
state its degree, type, and leading coefficient.**

1. $g(x) = ix + 7$
2. $s(x) = 2x^2 + x^{-1}$
3. $d(x) = 3\pi x^2$

4. Evaluate $g(x) = -4x^2 + 6$ when $x = 3$ using direct substitution. Check with
   synthetic substitution.

EXAMPLE 3
Graph a polynomial function

**Graph $f(x) = -2(x + 1)^2(x - 1)^2$, then use the graph to describe the
degree and the leading coefficient of the function.**

To graph the function, make a table of values and plot
the corresponding points. Connect the points with a
smooth curve and check the end behavior.

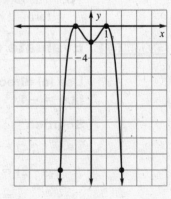

x	−2	−1	0	1	2
y	−18	0	−2	0	−18

The degree is even and the leading coefficient is
negative. So, $f(x) \to -\infty$ as $x \to -\infty$ and
$f(x) \to -\infty$ as $x \to +\infty$.

Exercises for Example 3

**Describe the end behavior of the graph of the polynomial function by
completing these statements: $f(x) \to$ _?_ as $x \to -\infty$ and $f(x) \to$ _?_ as
$x \to +\infty$.**

5. $f(x) = (x - 1)^2(x + 1)^2$
6. $f(x) = (x + 2)(x + 1)(x - 3)$

LESSON 5.2 Quick Catch-Up for Absent Students
For use with pages 336–345

The items checked below were covered in class on (date missed) _____

Activity 5.2: End Behavior of Polynomial Functions

_____ **Goal:** Discover how the end behavior of a polynomial function is related to its equation. (p. 336)

Lesson 5.2: Evaluate and Graph Polynomial Functions

_____ **Goal:** Evaluate and graph other polynomial functions. (pp. 337–341)

Material Covered:

_____ Example 1: Identify polynomial functions

_____ Example 2: Evaluate by direct substitution

_____ Guided Practice for Examples 1 and 2

_____ Example 3: Evaluate by synthetic substitution

_____ Avoid errors

_____ Reading

_____ Example 4: Standardized Test Practice

_____ Guided Practice for Examples 3 and 4

_____ Example 5: Graph polynomial functions

_____ Example 6: Solve a multi-step problem

_____ Guided Practice for Examples 5 and 6

Vocabulary:

polynomial, p. 337   polynomial function, p. 337

synthetic substitution, p. 338   end behavior, p. 339

_____ Other (specify)

_____

Homework and Additional Learning Support

_____ Textbook (specify) pp. 341–344

_____

_____ *Study Guide* worksheet (specify exercises)_____

_____ @*HomeTutor* for Lesson 5.2

Activity 5.2: Set a Good Viewing Window

_____ **Goal:** Learn to set a good viewing window for a polynomial function. (p. 345)

LESSON 5.2
Problem Solving Workshop: Worked Out Example
For use with pages 336–345

PROBLEM **Skid Distance** The skid distance D (in feet) of a car traveling on a gravel road is given by the model $D = 0.0565s^2$ where s is the speed of the car (in miles per hour). Graph the model. Use the graph to estimate the speed of a car that had a skid distance of 100 feet.

STEP 1 Read and Understand

What do you know?

The function that models skid distance

What do you want to find out?

The speed of a car that had a skid distance of 100 feet

STEP 2 Make a Plan Use what you know to make a table and graph the model.

STEP 3 Solve the Problem Make a table of values. The model only deals with positive values of s.

s	0	10	20	30	40
D	0	5.65	22.6	50.85	90.4

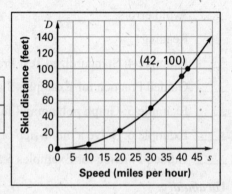

Plot the points and connect them with a smooth curve. Because the leading coefficient is positive and the degree is even, the graph rises to the right.

Examine the graph to see that $s \approx 42$ when $D = 100$. The speed of a car that had a skid distance of 100 feet was about 42 miles per hour.

STEP 4 Look Back You can find the speed of the car with a skid distance of 100 feet by solving the equation.

$$100 = 0.0565s^2 \qquad \text{Substitute 100 for } D.$$
$$1769.912 \approx s^2 \qquad \text{Divide each side by 0.0565.}$$
$$\pm 42.07 \approx s \qquad \text{Solve for } s.$$

Because the model only deals with positive values of s, the answer is correct.

PRACTICE **1. Shopping** The retail space in shopping centers in the United States from 1990 to 2003 can be modeled by $S = -0.076t^3 + 1.053t^2 + 110.937t + 4423$ where S is the amount of retail space (in millions of square feet) and t is the number of years since 1990. Graph the model. How much retail space will there be 2011?

2. Precipitation The average monthly precipitation p (in inches) in Duluth, Minnesota for each month of the year can be modeled by $p = 0.0034t^4 - 0.1013t^3 + 0.9086t^2 - 2.3246t + 2.6547$ where $t = 1$ represents January. Graph the model. According to the graph, what month(s) has an average precipitation of 4.22 inches?

Name _____   Date _____

Challenge Practice
For use with pages 336–345

In Exercises 1–4, use the following information.

You have learned that the slope of a line can be used to represent an average rate of change. For a nonlinear graph whose slope changes at each point, the average rate of change between any two points $(x_1, f(x_1))$ and $(x_2, f(x_2))$ is the slope of the line through the two points as shown below. The line through the two points is called the *secant line*, and the slope of this line is denoted as m_{sec}.

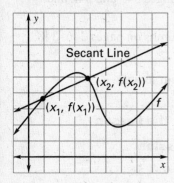

You can calculate the average rate of change of a function f from x_1 to x_2 using the following formula.

$$m_{sec} = \frac{f(x_2) - f(x_1)}{x_2 - x_1}$$

1. Consider the function given by $f(x) = -x^3 + 3x^2 + x - 3$. Find the average rate of change of the function from x_1 to x_2.

   a. $x_1 = 1, x_2 = 2$
   b. $x_1 = 1, x_2 = 1.8$
   c. $x_1 = 1, x_2 = 1.5$
   d. $x_1 = 1, x_2 = 1.1$
   e. $x_1 = 1, x_2 = 1.05$

2. Does the average rate of change seem to be approaching one value? If so, what value?

3. Find the equation of the secant line through the points $(x_1, f(x_1))$ and $(x_2, f(x_2))$ for parts (a)–(e) in Exercise 1.

4. Find the equation of the line through the point $(1, f(1))$ using your answer from Exercise 2 as the slope of the line.

LESSON 5.3 Teaching Guide

Key Concept

You will add, subtract, and multiply polynomials. You will use polynomial models to solve real-life problems.

Teaching the Lesson

Differentiating Instruction: See the Teacher's Edition side column notes on pages 347 and 348 and the notes on differentiating instruction in the *Algebra 2 Toolkit*.

Teaching Notes and Suggested Questions: See the Teacher's Edition side columns on pages 346–348.

Activity Generator: See the Activity Generator Support Manual.

Animated Algebra: You may want to include the animation on page 351 in your lesson.

Starting the Lesson

Motivate the Lesson The questions at the right guide students through a brief review of simplifying expressions and multiplying binomials in order to understand how to add, subtract, and multiply polynomials.

Alternative Lesson Starter

You may want to review prerequisite concepts, such as:

- simplifying expressions (p. 10)

- like terms (p. 12)

Questions to Start the Lesson

Simplify the expression.

1. $3x^2 - (6x + x^2) + 9 - 5x$

2. $5x + 6(x^2 - 3) - x^2$

3. $2x^2 + 4x(x + 2) - 5(x - 1)$

4. $(x - 6)(x - 5)$

5. $(3x + 4)(x + 9)$

6. $(2x + 5)(3x - 8)$

Common Student Errors

- Not distributing the subtraction sign when subtracting polynomials

  Tip Some students subtract only the first term of the second polynomial and add the other terms. Remind students that the minus sign affects all terms of the second polynomial.

- Trouble using the *square* and *cube of a binomial patterns*

  Tip Show students the similarities between the patterns. Point out that the powers of *a* are written in increasing order, whereas the powers of *b* are in decreasing order. The coefficients are symmetric and start and end with a 1. The exponent of the binomial becomes a coefficient when it is expanded. Finally, a sum results in all terms being added whereas a difference yields alternate sums and differences.

Teaching Strategy of the Day

Testing Return tests during the next class period. Review of the test is more effective if done while it is still fresh in students' minds.

LESSON 5.3 Lesson Plan continued
Standard Schedule: 1 day lesson   Block Schedule: 0.5 day lesson with 5.2

GOAL Add, subtract, and multiply polynomials.

State Standards _____

Focus and Motivate

Starting Options
_____ Homework Check (5.2): TE p. 341; Answer Transparencies
_____ Daily Homework Quiz (5.2): TE p. 344
_____ Warm-Up: TE p. 346 or Transparencies
_____ Starting the Lesson Questions: Teaching Guide
_____ Motivating the Lesson: TE p. 347

Teach

Teaching Options
_____ Essential Question: TE p. 346
_____ Alternative Lesson Openers: Electronic Classroom
_____ Classroom Activity: Activity Generator; Chapter Resource Book p. 28
_____ Examples 1–6: PE pp. 346–348
_____ Extra Examples 1–6 with Key Questions: TE pp. 347–348
_____ Real-Life Application: Chapter Resource Book p. 35
_____ Notetaking Guide pp. 138–140

Checking for Understanding
_____ Closing the Lesson: TE p. 348
_____ Guided Practice Exercises: PE pp. 346–348

Practice and Apply

Assigning Homework
_____ Basic: Day 1: SRH p. 983 Exs. 1–15 odd; pp. 349–352 Exs. 1, 2, 3–13 odd, 15–19, 26–31, 38–40, 47–50, 59–62, 66–78 even
_____ Average: Day 1: pp. 349–352 Exs. 1, 2, 4–14 even, 15, 20–23, 26, 27, 32–35, 41–43, 47–55 odd, 59–63, 65–79 odd
_____ Advanced: Day 1: pp. 349–352 Exs. 1, 2, 10–15, 23–25, 34–37, 44–47, 50–64*, 66–72 even, 75, 79
_____ Block: pp. 349–352 Exs. 1, 2, 4–14 even, 15, 20–23, 26, 27, 32–35, 41–43, 47–55 odd, 59–63, 65–79 odd (with 5.2)
_____ Practice Masters: Chapter Resource Book pp. 29–31 (Levels A, B, or C)

Assess and Reteach

Differentiating Instruction
_____ Study Guide: Chapter Resource Book pp. 32–33
_____ Tutorial Software
_____ Challenge: Chapter Resource Book p. 36
_____ Remediation and Intervention Package: _____
_____ English Language Learners Package: _____

Preparing for Standardized Tests
_____ Standardized Test Practice: PE pp. 349–351 Exs. 2, 15, 47, 56, 63

Assessing the Lesson
_____ Daily Homework Quiz (5.3): TE p. 352 or Transparencies

LESSON 5.3

LESSON 5.3 Investigating Algebra Activity: Square a Binomial

For use before Lesson 5.3

Materials: paper and pencil

QUESTION How can you discover the pattern of the square of a binomial?

EXPLORE Square a binomial

1. Use the FOIL method to find the product. An example has been done for you.

Expression	Expanded form	FOIL	Simplify
$(x + y)^2$	$(x + y)(x + y)$	$x^2 + xy + xy + y^2$	$x^2 + 2xy + y^2$

   a. $(2x + 3)^2$

   b. $(4x + 5y)^2$

   c. $(x - y)^2$

   d. $(2x - 3)^2$

   e. $(4x - 5y)^2$

DRAW CONCLUSIONS Use your observations to complete the following.

2. For each expression, what relationship do you notice between the first term of the binomial and the first term in the simplified expression?

3. For each expression, what relationship do you notice between the last term of the binomial and the last term in the simplified expression?

4. For each expression, what relationship do you notice between the two terms of the binomial and the second term in the simplified expression?

5. Compare the operations in the original expressions with the operations in the simplified expressions.

6. Describe a "shortcut" that can be used to square a binomial. In other words, how do you square a binomial without using the FOIL method? Provide an example to show how your "shortcut" works.

LESSON 5.3

Name _____ Date _____

Practice A
For use with pages 346–352

Add or subtract in vertical format.

1. $\quad 5x^3 + 2x^2 - x - 7$
    $+ \quad x^3 - 3x^2 + 4x - 2$

2. $\quad 4x^3 - 8x^2 - x + 5$
    $- (2x^3 \quad\quad + 7x - 4)$

3. $\quad 9x^2 \quad\quad + 6$
    $- (6x^2 - 5x - 10)$

Find the sum.

4. $(x^2 + 2) + (4x^2 - 5)$

5. $(5x^2 + 3x) + (x^2 - 6x)$

6. $(9b^2 + b - 2) + (-5b^2 - 2b + 8)$

7. $(11n^2 + 2n - 8) + (4n^2 - 5n + 7)$

8. $(15m^3 + 8m) + (2m^2 - 6m + 9)$

9. $(w^3 + 4w^2 - 10w + 7) + (-6w^3 + 5w - 10)$

Find the difference.

10. $(12x^3 + 15) - (10x^3 + 2)$

11. $(9c^2 - 2c) - (c^2 + 9)$

12. $(7y^2 - 7y + 6) - (3y^2 + 2y - 1)$

13. $(4z^2 + 3) - (z^3 - 5z + 2)$

14. $(6x^3 + 5x^2 - 10x + 1) - (-2x^3 - 3x^2 + 3x)$

15. $(t^4 - 3t + 18) - (-5t^4 + t^3 - 2t^2)$

Find the product.

16. $x(2x^2 + 3x - 1)$

17. $8y^3(y - 4)$

18. $(m + 6)(m - 1)$

19. $(c - 2)(c - 9)$

20. $(8z - 5)(z + 1)$

21. $(h - 3)(h^2 + 2h - 8)$

22. $(x - 7)(x + 7)$

23. $(s + 9)^2$

Write the area of the figure as a polynomial in standard form.

24.
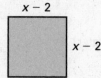
$x - 2$
$x - 2$

25.
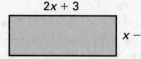
$2x + 3$
$x - 1$

26.
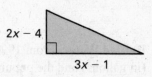
$2x - 4$
$3x - 1$

27. **Population** For 1995 through 2003, the male population M (in millions) and the female population F (in millions) of the United States can be modeled by

$M = -0.01098t^4 + 0.1284t^3 - 0.238t^2 + 1.11t + 128.4$ and

$F = -0.00877t^4 + 0.1025t^3 - 0.202t^2 + 1.16t + 134.6$

where t is the number of years since 1995. Write a model for the total population of the United States.

Name _____ Date _____

Practice B
For use with pages 346–352

Find the sum or difference.

1. $(2y^2 - 5y + 1) + (y^2 - y - 4)$

2. $(12x^2 + 8x - 3) - (11x^2 - x + 5)$

3. $(6m^3 - 5) - (m^3 + 4m^2 - 9m - 2)$

4. $(5s^4 - 2s^3 + 9) - (-2s^4 + 8s^2 - s + 2)$

5. $(7q - 3q^3) + (16 - 8q^3 + 5q^2 - q)$

6. $(-4z^4 + 6z - 9) + (11 - z^3 + 3z^2 + z^4)$

7. $(10v^4 - 2v^2 + 6v^3 - 7) - (9 - v + 2v^4)$

8. $(4x^5 + 3x^4 - 5x + 1) - (x^3 + 2x^4 - x^5 + 1)$

Find the product.

9. $2x^3(5x - 1)$

10. $(w - 8)(w - 1)$

11. $(c + 4)(c + 10)$

12. $(g + 9)(g - 2)$

13. $(y - 1)(y^2 + 6y - 2)$

14. $(n + 5)(2n^2 - n - 7)$

15. $(x - 3)^2$

16. $(4t + 1)^2$

17. $(z - 5)^3$

18. $(2f + 1)^3$

Write the volume of the figure as a polynomial in standard form.

19. $V = \ell wh$

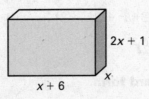

$2x + 1$

x

$x + 6$

20. $V = \frac{1}{3}\pi r^2 h$

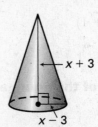

$x + 3$

$x - 3$

21. **Bottled Water** From 1990 to 1999, the per person consumption B of bottled water (in gallons) and the population P of the United States (in thousands) can be modeled by

$B = 0.0977t^2 + 0.186t + 7.86$ and

$P = 3226t + 250,359$

where t is the number of years since 1990. Write a model for the total consumption C of bottled water (in thousands of gallons). What was the total consumption of bottled water in 1998?

LESSON 5.3

Name _____ Date _____

Practice C

For use with pages 346–352

Find the sum or difference.

1. $(6w^3 + 2w^2 - 3w - 1) + (-5w^3 + 9w - 8)$

2. $(-x^4 + x^2 - x - x^3 + 1) + (x^2 - 2x^3 + 4x - 1)$

3. $(4m^4 - m^2 + 5m) - (-2m^3 + m^2 - 2m + 6)$

4. $(b^4 + 10b) - (4b^3 + 6b^2 - b + 5)$

5. $\left(\frac{2}{5}x^3 + 2x - 1\right) + \left(\frac{1}{5}x^3 - 9x + \frac{2}{3}\right)$

6. $\left(\frac{1}{4}c^3 - 3c^2 + \frac{5}{6}\right) - \left(\frac{1}{3}c^3 - 5c + \frac{2}{3}\right)$

7. $(\sqrt{2}\,d^2 - 6d + 1) - (2\sqrt{2}\,d^2 + d - 8)$

8. $(5x^3 - \sqrt{3}\,x^2 - 2x) + (3x^3 - \sqrt{3}\,x^2 + x)$

Find the product.

9. $2x^4(-3x^2 + 4x - 1)$

10. $(6s - 1)(5s + 2)$

11. $(2p + 1)(6p^2 - p + 8)$

12. $(-x^2 + 3)(x^2 + 6x - 2)$

13. $(2x^3 + x)(x^4 + 3x^3 - 2x^2 + 1)$

14. $(x^3 - 2x + 1)(x^3 + x^2 - 5)$

15. $(5q + 2)(-8q + 1)(q - 4)$

16. $(2x - y)(2x + y)$

17. $(2y + 3z)^3$

18. $\left(\frac{1}{2}x - \frac{1}{4}y\right)^2$

19. **Construction** Find a polynomial that represents the total number of square feet for the floor plan shown.

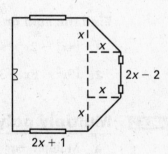

20. **Spending** From 1997 to 2002, the average annual amount spent on food F (in dollars) and the percent of that amount spent on food away from home P can be modeled by

    $F = 129.4t + 4759$ and

    $P = -0.06875t^4 + 0.833t^3 - 3.32t^2 + 4.8t + 40$

    where t is the number of years since 1997.

    a. Write a model for the average annual amount spent on food away from home A. (*Hint:* Divide P by 100 before writing your model.)

    b. Explain why it is necessary to divide P by 100 before writing your model.

    c. What was the average annual amount spent on food away from home in 2000?

Study Guide

LESSON 5.3

For use with pages 346–352

GOAL Add, subtract, and multiply polynomials.

EXAMPLE 1 ## Add and subtract polynomials

a. Add $x^3 - 2x + 8$ and $7x^2 + 2x - 5$ in a vertical format.

$$
\begin{array}{r}
x^3 \qquad - 2x + 8 \\
+ \qquad 7x^2 + 2x - 5 \\
\hline
x^3 + 7x^2 \qquad + 3
\end{array}
$$

b. Add $7x^2 + 2x - 5$ and $x^3 - 2x^2 + 4x + 8$ in a horizontal format.

$$(7x^2 + 2x - 5) + (x^3 - 2x^2 + 4x + 8) = x^3 + 7x^2 - 2x^2 + 2x + 4x - 5 + 8$$
$$= x^3 + 5x^2 + 6x + 3$$

c. Subtract $y^2 - 2y + 7$ from $2y^2 + 6y - 2$ in a vertical format. Align like terms, then add the opposite of the subtracted polynomial.

$$
\begin{array}{l}
2y^2 + 6y - 2 \\
-(y^2 - 2y + 7)
\end{array}
\qquad \longrightarrow \qquad
\begin{array}{r}
2y^2 + 6y - 2 \\
+ -y^2 + 2y - 7 \\
\hline
y^2 + 8y - 9
\end{array}
$$

d. Subtract $6x^3 + 5x^2 - 7x$ from $5x^3 - x^2 + 10x$ in a horizontal format. Write the opposite of the subtracted polynomial, then add like terms.

$$(5x^3 - x^2 + 10x) - (6x^3 + 5x^2 - 7x) = 5x^3 - x^2 + 10x - 6x^3 - 5x^2 + 7x$$
$$= -x^3 - 6x^2 + 17x$$

Exercises for Example 1

Find the sum or difference.

1. $(4x^3 - 2x^2 + 5) + (-x^3 - x^2 + 4x - 2)$

2. $(9x^2 - 8x + 3) - (2x^2 + x - 4)$

EXAMPLE 2 ## Multiply polynomials vertically and horizontally

a. Multiply $-x^2 - 2x + 7$ and $x + 2$ in a vertical format.

$$
\begin{array}{r}
-x^2 - 2x + 7 \\
\times \qquad x + 2 \\
\hline
-2x^2 - 4x + 14 \\
-x^3 - 2x^2 + 7x \\
\hline
-x^3 - 4x^2 + 3x + 14
\end{array}
$$

Multiply $-x^2 - 2x + 7$ by 2.

Multiply $-x^2 - 2x + 7$ by x.

Combine like terms.

b. Multiply $(x + 3)(x - 1)(x + 2)$ in a horizontal format.

$$(x + 3)(x - 1)(x + 2) = (x^2 + 2x - 3)(x + 2)$$
$$= (x^2 + 2x - 3)x + (x^2 + 2x - 3)2$$
$$= x^3 + 2x^2 - 3x + 2x^2 + 4x - 6$$
$$= x^3 + 4x^2 + x - 6$$

Study Guide *continued*
For use with pages 346–352

Exercises for Example 2

Find the product.

3. $(z^2 - 5z + 3)(z - 1)$

4. $(x - 2)(x - 1)(x + 3)$

EXAMPLE 3 Use special product patterns

a. $(6a + 1)^2 = (6a)^2 + 2(6a)(1) + 12$ Square of a binomial

$\qquad\qquad = 36a^2 + 12a + 1$

b. $(5z + 2)(5z - 2) = (5z)^2 - 22$ Sum and difference

$\qquad\qquad\qquad = 25z^2 - 4$

c. $(2y + 3)^3 = (2y)^3 + 3(2y)^2(3) + 3(2y)(3)^2 + 3^3$ Cube of a binomial

$\qquad\qquad = 8y^3 + 36y^2 + 54y + 27$

Exercises for Example 3

Find the product.

5. $(x + 2)^3$

6. $(7y - 2)^2$

7. $(4d + 3)(4d - 3)$

8. $(2a + 5)^2$

EXAMPLE 4 Use polynomial models

Volume of a Cylinder The volume of a cylinder is modeled by $V = \pi r^2 h$ where r is the radius of the circular base and h is the height of the cylinder. Write the volume of the cylinder as a polynomial in standard form when $r = (x + 1)$ and $h = (x + 2)$. Then find the volume when $x = 1$.

Solution

$V = \pi r^2 h$ Formula for volume of a cylinder

$ = \pi(x + 1)^2(x + 2)$ Substitute $r = x + 1$ and $h = x + 2$.

$ = \pi(x^2 + 2x + 1)(x + 2)$ Square of a binomial

$ = \pi(x^3 + 2x^2 + x + 2x^2 + 4x + 2)$ Distributive property

$ = \pi(x^3 + 4x^2 + 5x + 2)$ Combine like terms.

The volume is written as the product of π and a polynomial written in standard form. When $x = 1$, $V = \pi \left[1^3 + 4(1)^2 + 5(1) + 2 \right] = 12\pi$.

Exercise for Example 4

9. Rework Example 4 where $r = (x + 2)$ and $h = (x + 3)$. Then find the volume when $x = 1$.

LESSON 5.3 Quick Catch-Up for Absent Students

For use with pages 346–352

The items checked below were covered in class on (date missed) _____

Lesson 5.3: Add, Subtract, and Multiply Polynomials

_____ **Goal:** Add, subtract, and multiply polynomials. (pp. 346–348)

Material Covered:

_____ Example 1: Add polynomials vertically and horizontally

_____ Review simplifying

_____ Example 2: Subtract polynomials vertically and horizontally

_____ Guided Practice for Examples 1 and 2

_____ Example 3: Multiply polynomials vertically and horizontally

_____ Example 4: Multiply three binomials

_____ Avoid errors

_____ Example 5: Use special product patterns

_____ Guided Practice for Examples 3, 4, and 5

_____ Example 6: Use polynomial models

_____ Guided Practice for Example 6

_____ Other (specify)

_____

Homework and Additional Learning Support

_____ Textbook (specify) pp. 349–352

_____

_____ *Study Guide* worksheet (specify exercises)_____

_____ *@HomeTutor* for Lesson 5.3

Name _____ Date _____

Real-Life Application: When Will I Ever Use This?

For use with pages 346–352

Constructing a Pyramid

For a class project, you and your classmates are constructing two pyramids using aluminum cans. One of your pyramids will have a triangular base and the other will have a square base as shown below.

The formula for the total number of cans C in a triangular-base pyramid with n layers is $C = \frac{1}{6}n^3 + \frac{1}{2}n^2 + \frac{1}{3}n$. For a square-base pyramid, it is $C = \frac{1}{3}n^3 + \frac{1}{2}n^2 + \frac{1}{6}n$.

1. Complete the table shown below for each type of pyramid. Round your answers to the nearest integer if necessary.

Number of layers, *n*	2	3	4	5	6	7	8	9	10	11	12
Total number of cans in pyramid, *C*											

2. Sketch the graphs of $C = \frac{1}{6}n^3 + \frac{1}{2}n^2 + \frac{1}{3}n$ and $C = \frac{1}{3}n^3 + \frac{1}{2}n^2 + \frac{1}{6}n$ for $1 \le n \le 12$. How do the graphs compare?

3. Suppose you are constructing a triangular-base pyramid and you already have n layers stacked. In terms of n, how many total cans will be in the pyramid if another layer is added? Write your result in standard form.

4. Using the expression found in Exercise 3, explain how to find the number of cans in the added layer in terms of n. Write your result in standard form.

5. Redo Exercise 3 for a square-base pyramid.

6. Using the expression found in Exercise 5, explain how to find the number of cans in the added layer of a square-base pyramid in terms of n. Write your result in standard form.

7. How many more cans would be in a 20-layer square-base pyramid than a 20-layer triangular-base pyramid?

8. How many more cans would be in the sixteenth layer of a square-base pyramid than the eighteenth layer of a triangular-base pyramid?

Name _____ Date _____

Challenge Practice

For use with pages 346–352

In Exercises 1–4, simplify the expression. (Assume that all variables represent positive integers.)

1. $3x^r(5x^{2r} + 4x^{3r-1})$

2. $5x^r(4x^{r+2} - 3x^r)$

3. $(6x^m - 5)(2x^{2m} - 3)$

4. $(x^{3m} - x^{2m})(x^{2m} + 2x^{4m})$

5. Find the product $(a + b + c)^2$.

6. Use the result of Exercise 5 to find each product.

 a. $(x^2 + 3x - 2)^2$

 b. $(4x - 5y + 7)^2$

In Exercises 7 and 8, use the area model to write two different expressions that represent the total area of the figure. Equate the two expressions and identify the algebraic property that is illustrated.

7.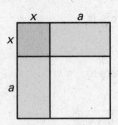

8.

9. **Compound Interest** The amount A in a savings account t years after a principal of P dollars is invested at annual interest rate r (expressed as a decimal) compounded annually is given by $A = P(1 + r)^2$. (*Compound interest* is interest paid on the principal investment and on previously earned interest.) Carey and Emma made the following deposits in their savings accounts.

Carey		
Date	**Transaction**	**Amount**
1/1/2004	Deposit	$500
1/1/2005	Deposit	$800
1/1/2006	Deposit	$600

Emma		
Date	**Transaction**	**Amount**
1/1/2004	Deposit	$750
1/1/2005	Deposit	$500
1/1/2006	Deposit	$900

 a. Write polynomial expressions in standard form that represent the total amount in Carey's account on January 1, 2007 and the total amount in Emma's account on January 1, 2007.

 b. Write a polynomial expression in standard form that represents the total amount in both accounts on January 1, 2007.

 c. If the interest rate for Carey's savings account is 3% and the interest rate for Emma's savings account is 2.5%, whose account is worth more on January 1, 2007?

Teaching Guide
LESSON 5.4

Key Concept
You will factor polynomials using several techniques including factoring by finding a common monomial factor, factoring using the sum or difference of two cubes, and factoring by grouping. You will solve some higher degree polynomial equations using the zero product property.

Teaching the Lesson
Differentiating Instruction: See the Teacher's Edition side column notes on page 354 and the notes on differentiating instruction in the *Algebra 2 Toolkit*.

Teaching Notes and Suggested Questions: See the Teacher's Edition side columns on pages 353–356.

Activity Generator: See the Activity Generator Support Manual.

Starting the Lesson

Connect to Prior Learning One way to introduce the concept of factoring and solving polynomials is to apply it to finding volume. Use the activity at right and the diagram below.

The volume of the box is 96 cm^2.

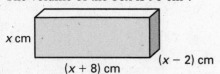

x cm
(x + 8) cm
(x − 2) cm

Alternative Lesson Starter

Be sure that students recall the following ideas:

- Solve $x^2 + bx + c = 0$ by factoring. (p. 252)

- Solve $ax^2 + bx + c = 0$ by factoring. (p. 259)

Questions to Start the Lesson

1. Write an equation to represent the volume of the box. The equation is in factored form. Why can't you use the equation in this form to solve for x?

2. Rewrite the equation in standard form. The equation should be of the form $ax^3 + bx^2 + cx + d = 0$.

3. Factor $ax^3 + bx^2$, where a and b are the coefficients from the equation. What is the result? Factor $cx + d$, where c and d are the coefficients from the equation. What is the result? What similarity do you notice?

4. Use your answer from Exercise 3 to rewrite the equation from Exercise 2 in factored form. What three solutions do you get from the factors? Which solution makes sense in the context of the box? What are the dimensions of the box?

Common Student Errors

- Some students stop factoring too soon

  Tip Remind students that they must examine the resulting factors looking for any expressions they might be able to factor again.

Example: $4x^3 - 4xy^2$

$= 4x(x^2 - y^2)$ After factoring out the common monomial term, the remaining binomial can still be factored.

$= 4x(x + y)(x - y)$ Factored completely.

Teaching Strategy of the Day

Motivating Students Start class with two or three review problems from a previous chapter. Frequent review of past material will be valuable for students who take cumulative tests during or at the end of the school year.

Teacher's Name _____ Class _____ Room _____ Date _____

LESSON 5.4 — Lesson Plan *continued*
Standard Schedule: 1 day lesson   Block Schedule: 0.5 day lesson with 5.5

GOAL **Factor and solve other polynomial equations.**

State Standards _____

Focus and Motivate

Starting Options
_____ Homework Check (5.3): TE p. 349; Answer Transparencies
_____ Daily Homework Quiz (5.3): TE p. 352
_____ Warm-Up: TE p. 353 or Transparencies
_____ Starting the Lesson Questions: Teaching Guide
_____ Motivating the Lesson: TE p. 354

Teach

Teaching Options
_____ Essential Question: TE p. 353
_____ Alternative Lesson Openers: Electronic Classroom
_____ Classroom Activity: Activity Generator
_____ Examples 1–6: PE pp. 353–356
_____ Extra Examples 1–6 with Key Questions: TE pp. 354–356
_____ Interdisciplinary Application: Chapter Resource Book p. 45
_____ Notetaking Guide pp. 141–143

Checking for Understanding
_____ Closing the Lesson: TE p. 356
_____ Guided Practice Exercises: PE pp. 354–356

Practice and Apply

Assigning Homework
_____ Basic: Day 1: EP p. 1013 Exs. 3–16; pp. 356–359 Exs. 1, 2, 3–29 odd, 30–34,
   41–44, 58–62, 66, 68, 70, 76
_____ Average: Day 1: pp. 356–359 Exs. 1, 2, 4–8 even, 9, 10–28 even, 30, 31, 35–37, 41,
   45–47, 51–53, 60–63, 67, 74, 77
_____ Advanced: Day 1: pp. 356–359 Exs. 1, 2, 7–9, 15–17, 21–23, 27–29, 38–41,
   47–57*, 60–65*, 69, 75, 79
_____ Block: pp. 356–359 Exs. 1, 2, 4–8 even, 9, 10–28 even, 30, 31, 35–37, 41, 45–47,
   51–53, 60–63, 67, 74, 77 (with 5.5)
_____ Practice Masters: Chapter Resource Book pp. 39–41 (Levels A, B, or C)

Assess and Reteach

Differentiating Instruction
_____ Study Guide: Chapter Resource Book pp. 42–43
_____ Tutorial Software
_____ Challenge: Chapter Resource Book p. 46
_____ Remediation and Intervention Package: _____
_____ English Language Learners Package: _____

Preparing for Standardized Tests
_____ Standardized Test Practice: PE pp. 356–359 Exs. 2, 9, 41, 63, 64

Assessing the Lesson
_____ Daily Homework Quiz (5.4): TE p. 359 or Transparencies

Practice A
For use with pages 353–359

Find the greatest common factor of the terms in the polynomial.

1. $4x^4 + 12x^3$ **2.** $10y^2 + 4y - 64$ **3.** $16x^5 - 8x$

4. $32n^5 - 64n^3 + 16n^2$ **5.** $15p^6 - 5p^4 - 10p^2$ **6.** $36c^9 + 13$

Match the polynomial with its factorization.

7. $3x^2 + 11x + 6$ **A.** $2x^3(x + 2)(x - 2)(x^2 + 3)$

8. $x^3 - 4x^2 + 4x - 16$ **B.** $2x(x + 4)(x - 4)$

9. $125x^3 - 216$ **C.** $(3x + 2)(x + 3)$

10. $2x^7 - 2x^5 - 24x^3$ **D.** $(x^2 + 4)(x - 4)$

11. $2x^5 + 4x^4 - 4x^3 - 8x^2$ **E.** $2x^2(x^2 - 2)(x + 2)$

12. $2x^3 - 32x$ **F.** $(5x - 6)(25x^2 + 30x + 36)$

Factor the sum or difference of cubes.

13. $s^3 - 1$ **14.** $q^3 + 1$

15. $x^3 - 27$ **16.** $a^3 + 125$

17. $h^3 + 64$ **18.** $8y^3 - 125$

Factor the polynomial by grouping.

19. $x^3 + 2x^2 + 3x + 6$ **20.** $z^3 - z^2 + 5z - 5$

21. $f^3 + 4f^2 + f + 4$ **22.** $m^3 - 2m^2 + 4m - 8$

23. $2x^4 - x^3 + 6x - 3$ **24.** $t^3 - 2t^2 - 9t + 18$

Find the real-number solutions of the equation.

25. $w^2 - 3w = 0$ **26.** $v^3 + 5v^2 = 0$

27. $x^2 - 5x + 6 = 0$ **28.** $d^2 - 16 = 0$

29. $10s^3 = 30s^2$ **30.** $x^3 + x^2 - 9x - 9 = 0$

Match the equation for volume with the appropriate solid.

31. $V = x^3 - 4x$ **32.** $V = x^3 - 4x^2 + 4x$ **33.** $V = x^4 - 16$

A.

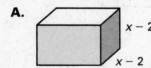

$x - 2$

$x - 2$

x

B.

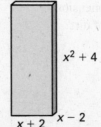

$x^2 + 4$

$x + 2$ $x - 2$

C.

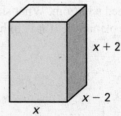

$x + 2$

$x - 2$

x

LESSON 5.4

Practice B

For use with pages 353–359

Factor the sum or difference of cubes.

1. $x^3 + 125$

2. $y^3 - 8$

3. $64n^3 - 27$

4. $27g^3 + 343$

5. $2w^3 + 54$

6. $40v^3 - 625$

Factor the polynomial by grouping.

7. $r^3 - 3r^2 + 6r - 18$

8. $x^3 + 6x^2 + 7x + 42$

9. $c^3 + 4c^2 - 9c - 36$

10. $z^3 - 2z^2 - 16z + 32$

11. $25p^3 - 25p^2 - p + 1$

12. $9m^3 + 18m^2 - 4m - 8$

Factor the polynomial in quadratic form.

13. $x^4 - 36$

14. $c^4 - 81$

15. $x^4 + x^2 - 20$

16. $6y^6 - 5y^3 - 4$

Factor the polynomial completely.

17. $x^6 - 4$

18. $d^4 - 7d^2 + 10$

19. $24q^3 - 81$

20. $a^6 + 7a^3 + 6$

21. $-4x^4 + 26x^2 - 30$

22. $2b^4 + 14b^3 - 16b - 112$

Find the real-number solutions of the equation.

23. $n^4 + 6n^3 = 0$

24. $4k^3 = 9k^2$

25. $x^3 + 2x^2 - 25x - 50 = 0$

26. $6w^3 + 30w^2 - 18w - 90 = 0$

27. $y^4 - 14y^2 + 45 = 0$

28. $3r^5 + 15r^3 - 18r = 0$

29. Write a binomial that can be factored either as the difference of two squares or as the difference of two cubes. Show the complete factorization of your binomial.

30. **City Park** You are designing a marble planter for a city park. You want the length of the planter to be six times the height, and the width to be three times the height. The sides should be one foot thick. Because the planter will be on the sidewalk, it does not need a bottom. What should the outer dimensions of the planter be if it is to hold 4 cubic feet of dirt?

Practice C
For use with pages 353–359

Factor the polynomial completely using any method.

1. $x^3 - 512$

2. $2a^3 + 432$

3. $7h^3 + 448$

4. $-3c^3 + 24$

5. $12x^3 - 6x^2 + 2x - 1$

6. $3k^4 + 27k^3 - 7k - 63$

7. $3n^3 - 10n^2 - 48n + 160$

8. $x^6 + x^5 - x^4 - x^3$

9. $y^4 - 81$

10. $2z^4 - 1250$

11. $6a^4 + 13a^2 - 5$

12. $6b^4 - 17b^2 - 28$

13. $r^5 + r^3 - r^2 + 1$

14. $-4w^8 - 8w^6 + 4w^4 + 8w^2$

15. $a^6b^3 + 125$

16. $2ac^2 - 5bc^2 - 2ad^2 + 5bd^2$

Find the real-number solutions of the equation.

17. $x^3 + 1000 = 0$

18. $27g^3 - 8 = 0$

19. $6v^3 = 384$

20. $p^3 + 4p^2 - 9p = 36$

21. $125q^4 - 27 = 125q^3 - 27q$

22. $s^4 - 11s^2 + 28 = 0$

23. $162y^4 = 2$

24. $m^6 - 64 = 0$

25. $3z^{11} - 3z^5 = 0$

26. $16h^5 - 25h^3 + 9h = 0$

27. $12n^7 + 2n^5 = 30n^3$

28. $6r^7 + 6r^5 = 9r^6 + 9r^4$

29. Write a polynomial that can be factored using grouping and the sum of cubes. Show the complete factorization of your polynomial.

30. **Theater** A stage crew is assembling a three-level semi-circular platform on a stage for a performance. The platform has the dimensions shown in the diagram and a total volume of 448π cubic feet.

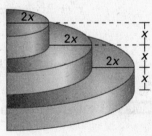

a. What is the volume, in terms of x, of each of the three levels of the platform?

b. Use what you know about the total volume to write an equation involving x.

c. Solve the equation from part (b).

d. Use your solution from part (c) to calculate the dimensions (radius and height) of each of the levels of the platform.

Study Guide
For use with pages 353–359

GOAL **Factor and solve other polynomial equations.**

Vocabulary

A polynomial with two or more terms is a **prime polynomial** if it cannot be written as a product of polynomials of lesser degree using only integer coefficients and constants and if the only common factors of its terms are -1 and 1.

A polynomial is **factored completely** if it is written as a monomial or the product of a monomial and one or more prime polynomials.

For some polynomials you can **factor by grouping** pairs of terms that have a common monomial factor.

An expression of the form $au^2 + bu + c$, where u is any expression in x, is said to be in **quadratic form**.

EXAMPLE 1 **Factor the sum or difference of two cubes**

Factor the polynomial completely.

$$
\begin{aligned}
\textbf{a.}\quad 4x^4 - 108x &= 4x(x^3 - 27) && \text{Factor common monomial.} \\
&= 4x(x - 3)(x^2 + 3x + 9) && \text{Difference of two cubes} \\
\textbf{b.}\quad 2b^3 + 16a^3 &= 2(b^3 + 8a^3) && \text{Factor common monomial.} \\
&= 2(b + 2a)(b^2 - 2ab + 4a^2) && \text{Sum of two cubes}
\end{aligned}
$$

EXAMPLE 2 **Factor by grouping**

Factor the polynomial $x^3 + 2x^2 - x - 2$ completely.

$$
\begin{aligned}
x^3 + 2x^2 - x - 2 &= x^2(x + 2) - 1(x + 2) && \text{Factor by grouping.} \\
&= (x^2 - 1)(x + 2) && \text{Distributive property} \\
&= (x + 1)(x - 1)(x + 2) && \text{Difference of two squares}
\end{aligned}
$$

EXAMPLE 3 **Factor polynomials in quadratic form**

Factor completely: (a) $3x^8 + 18x^5 + 24x^2$ and (b) $81g^4 - 256$.

$$
\begin{aligned}
\textbf{a.}\quad 3x^8 + 18x^5 + 24x^2 &= 3x^2(x^6 + 6x^3 + 8) && \text{Factor common monomial.} \\
&= 3x^2(x^3 + 2)(x^3 + 4) && \text{Factor trinomial in quadratic form.} \\
\textbf{b.}\quad 81g^4 - 256 &= (9g^2)^2 - (16)^2 && \text{Write as difference of two squares.} \\
&= (9g^2 + 16)(9g^2 - 16) && \text{Difference of two squares} \\
&= (9g^2 + 16)(3g + 4)(3g - 4) && \text{Difference of two squares}
\end{aligned}
$$

Study Guide *continued*
For use with pages 353–359

EXAMPLE 4 **Find real-number solutions**

Find the real-number solutions of the equation $x^4 - 7x^2 = -12$.

$x^4 - 7x^2 = -12$	Write original equation.
$x^4 - 7x^2 + 12 = 0$	Write in standard form.
$(x^2 - 4)(x^2 - 3) = 0$	Factor trinomial.
$(x + 2)(x - 2)(x^2 - 3) = 0$	Difference of two squares
$x = -2, x = 2, x = \sqrt{3},$ or $x = -\sqrt{3}$	Zero product property

EXAMPLE 5 **Solve a polynomial equation**

The dimensions (in inches) of a jewelry box are: length $4x$, width $(x - 1)$, and height $(x - 2)$. If the volume of the box is 24 cubic inches, find the dimensions of the box.

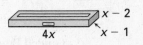

Solution

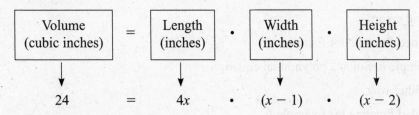

Volume (cubic inches)	=	Length (inches)	·	Width (inches)	·	Height (inches)
24	=	$4x$	·	$(x - 1)$	·	$(x - 2)$

$24 = (4x)(x - 1)(x - 2)$	Write equation.
$0 = 4x^3 - 12x^2 + 8x - 24$	Write in standard form.
$0 = 4x^2(x - 3) + 8(x - 3)$	Factor by grouping.
$0 = (4x^2 + 8)(x - 3)$	Distributive property

The only real solution is $x = 3$. The jewelry box is 12 inches long, 2 inches wide, and 1 inch high.

Exercises for Examples 1, 2, 3, 4, and 5

Factor the polynomial completely.

1. $7x^5 - 56x^2$ **2.** $128y^6 + 2$ **3.** $x^3 - 3x^2 - 4x + 12$

4. $y^3 + 7y^2 - 9y - 63$ **5.** $3b^6 + 6b^4 + 3b^2$ **6.** $z^8 - 16$

Find the real-number solutions of the equation.

7. $x^4 - 3x^2 + 2 = 0$ **8.** $x^5 - 8x^3 = -12x$ **9.** $x^5 - 12x^3 = -27x$

10. The dimensions (in inches) of a jewelry box are: length $2x$, width $(x - 1)$, and height $(x - 3)$. If the volume of the box is 24 cubic inches, find the dimensions of the box.

Quick Catch-Up for Absent Students

LESSON 5.4

For use with pages 353–361

The items checked below were covered in class on (date missed) _____

Lesson 5.4: Factor and Solve Polynomial Equations

_____ **Goal:** Factor and solve other polynomial equations. (pp. 353–356)

Material Covered:

_____ Example 1: Find a common monomial factor

_____ Example 2: Factor the sum or difference of two cubes

_____ Guided Practice for Examples 1 and 2

_____ Example 3: Factor by grouping

_____ Avoid errors

_____ Example 4: Factor polynomials in quadratic form

_____ Identify quadratic form

_____ Guided Practice for Examples 3 and 4

_____ Example 5: Standardized Test Practice

_____ Avoid errors

_____ Guided Practice for Example 5

_____ Example 6: Solve a polynomial equation

_____ Another way

_____ Guided Practice for Example 6

Vocabulary:

factored completely, p. 353   factor by grouping, p. 354

quadratic form, p. 355

_____ Other (specify)

_____

Homework and Additional Learning Support

_____ Textbook (specify) pp. 356–359

_____

_____ *Study Guide* worksheet (specify exercises)_____

_____ *@HomeTutor* for Lesson 5.4

Problem Solving Workshop 5.4

_____ Exercises 1–10 (pp. 360–361)

Interdisciplinary Application

For use with pages 353–359

Aquariums

Biology Aquariums can range in size anywhere from a 20-gallon home aquarium to large buildings that contain exhibits of aquatic wildlife. Large tanks, called oceanariums, can hold more than 5 million gallons of water. Public aquariums are popular tourist attractions that are visited by millions of people each year. They also can serve as important research, education, and conservation centers. These public aquariums are fascinating in the fact that only a pane of glass can separate an observer from a killer whale or shark.

Aquarists, marine biologists, and mammologists are just some of the people that help maintain public aquariums. It is their responsibility to not only maintain the living conditions inside the aquarium but to feed and nourish the wildlife that live there.

In Exercises 1 and 2, use the following information.

The Tennessee Aquarium in Chattanooga, Tennessee is the largest freshwater aquarium in the world with 450,000 gallons of water in 24 exhibits. The 130,000 square feet of the aquarium are home to more than 9000 creatures. An interesting fact is that 300,000 crickets, about 400,000 worms, and 15,000 pounds of seafood are devoured by the aquarium's wildlife each year.

1. How many gallons of water, on average, does each exhibit in the aquarium have?

2. Suppose the Tennessee Aquarium is opening a new saltwater exhibit that will have tropical fish from around the world. Three of the new rectangular aquariums being ordered are described below.

   Aquarium 1 (180-gallon tank): The aquarium has a length of x inches, a height and width that are both 48 inches less than the length, and a volume of 41,472 cubic inches. Write a polynomial in standard form to describe the volume of the aquarium. Then find its dimensions.

   Aquarium 2 (300-gallon tank): The aquarium has dimensions of x feet long, $(x - 6)$ feet wide, and $(x - 5.5)$ feet high. The volume of the aquarium is 40 cubic feet. Write a polynomial in standard form to describe the volume of the aquarium. Then find its dimensions.

   Aquarium 3 (125-gallon tank): The length of this aquarium is three times its height and its width is 4 inches more than the height. The volume of the aquarium is 28,800 cubic inches. Write a polynomial in standard form to describe the volume of the aquarium. Then find its dimensions.

LESSON 5.4 Challenge Practice
For use with pages 353–359

**In Exercises 1–6, factor the polynomial completely.
(Assume that n is a positive integer.)**

1. $4y^{2n} - 4y^n - 3$

2. $3x^{2n} - 16x^n - 12$

3. $2x^{3n} + 16y^{3n}$

4. $x^{3n} - y^{2n}$

5. $-a^5b - a^3b^3 + 4a^2b + 4b^3 - 2a^3b - 2ab^3 + a^2 + b^2$

6. $6a^3b - 3ab^4 + 2a^4b^2 - a^2b^5 - 12a^2b + 6b^4 + 2a^2 - b^3$

In Exercises 7–10, write a polynomial equation that has the given solutions.

7. $-2, 1, 2$

8. $-4, -3, 0, 3$

9. $-6, \pm\sqrt{5}$

10. $0, 5, \pm2\sqrt{3}$

In Exercises 11 and 12, solve the system of equations using the substitution method. Check your solutions.

11. $y = x^3 + 2x^2 - 2x + 4$
    $y = x + 10$

12. $y = 4x^4 + 2x^3 - 36x^2 + 11$
    $y = 2x^3 + 29x^2 - 5$

13. **Propane Tank** An industrial propane tank is formed by adjoining two hemispheres to the ends of a right circular cylinder. The length of the cylindrical portion of the tank is 4 times the radius of the hemispherical components, as shown in the figure.

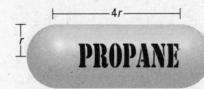

a. Write a function that represents the total volume V of the tank in terms of r.

b. What is the domain of the function from part (a)?

c. What is the radius and length of the cylindrical portion of the tank if the total volume of the tank is 144π cubic feet?

LESSON 5.5 Teaching Guide

Key Concept

You will use the factor theorem and synthetic division to factor or find the zeros of polynomials.

Teaching the Lesson

Differentiating Instruction: See the Teacher's Edition side column notes on page 363 and the notes on differentiating instruction in the *Algebra 2 Toolkit*.

Teaching Notes and Suggested Questions: See the Teacher's Edition side columns on pages 362–365.

Activity Generator: See the Activity Generator Support Manual.

Starting the Lesson

Connect to Prior Learning One way to introduce polynomial long division is by reviewing long division with numbers and pointing out the similarities. The example at right is one you might use to demonstrate.

Alternative Lesson Starter

You may want to review prerequisite concepts, such as:

- solving equations (p. 252 and p. 259)

- evaluate polynomials using synthetic substitution (p. 337)

Questions to Start the Lesson

1. Fill in the missing digits on the grid below. What is the dividend? the divisor? the quotient? the remainder?

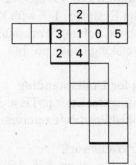

2. How would you use multiplication to check the result of this division?

3. How would the results be different if you changed 3105 to 315? What is the importance of the zero as a placeholder?

Common Student Errors

- Confusing *synthetic evaluation* with *synthetic division* and not knowing what sign to use for *k*

Tip Remind students that for *synthetic division* they must write the *opposite of the constant term* of the divisor.

Teaching Strategy of the Day

Motivating Students When grading a student's notebook, keep the grading scale simple, "passing" or "needs improvement"; "+" or "−".

LESSON 5.5

<table>
<tr><td>LESSON
5.5</td></tr>
</table>

Lesson Plan *continued*
Standard Schedule: 2 day lesson   *Block Schedule: 0.5 day lesson with 5.4, and 0.5 day with 5.6*

GOAL   **Use theorems to factor polynomials.**

State Standards _____

Focus and Motivate

Starting Options
_____ Homework Check (5.4): TE p. 357; Answer Transparencies
_____ Daily Homework Quiz (5.4): TE p. 359
_____ Warm-Up: TE p. 362 or Transparencies
_____ Starting the Lesson Questions: Teaching Guide
_____ Motivating the Lesson: TE p. 363

Teach

Teaching Options
_____ Essential Question: TE p. 362
_____ Alternative Lesson Openers: Electronic Classroom
_____ Classroom Activity: Activity Generator
_____ Examples 1–6: PE pp. 362–365
_____ Extra Examples 1–6 with Key Questions: TE pp. 363–365
_____ Problem Solving Workshop: Mixed Problem Solving: Chapter Resource Book p. 55
_____ Notetaking Guide pp. 144–146

Checking for Understanding
_____ Closing the Lesson: TE p. 365
_____ Guided Practice Exercises: PE pp. 363–365

Practice and Apply

Assigning Homework
_____ Basic: Day 1: pp. 366–368 Exs. 1–20, 47–50, 57–60; Day 2: pp. 366–368 Exs. 21–35, 41–44, 51–56
_____ Average: Day 1: pp. 366–368 Exs. 1, 2, 4–10, 12–20, 36, 37, 47–50, 57–60; Day 2: pp. 366–368 Exs. 23–28, 31–35, 38, 39, 41–45, 51–56
_____ Advanced: Day 1: pp. 366–368 Exs. 1–18, 36, 37, 47–50, 57–60; Day 2: pp. 366–368 Exs. 24–28, 32–35, 38–46*, 51–56
_____ Block: pp. 366–368 Exs. 1, 2, 4–10, 12–20, 36, 37, 47–50, 57–60 (with 5.4); pp. 366–368 Exs. 23–28, 31–35, 38, 39, 41–45, 51–56 (with 5.6)
_____ Practice Masters: Chapter Resource Book pp. 49–51 (Levels A, B, or C)

Assess and Reteach

Differentiating Instruction
_____ Study Guide: Chapter Resource Book pp. 52–53
_____ Tutorial Software
_____ Challenge: Chapter Resource Book p. 57
_____ Remediation and Intervention Package: _____
_____ English Language Learners Package: _____

Preparing for Standardized Tests
_____ Standardized Test Practice: PE pp. 366–368 Exs. 2, 35, 39, 44, 45

Assessing the Lesson
_____ Daily Homework Quiz (5.5): TE p. 368 or Transparencies

Name _____   Date _____

LESSON 5.5 **Practice A**
For use with pages 362–368

Write the divisor, dividend, quotient, and remainder represented by the synthetic division.

1.

$$
\begin{array}{r|rrrr}
-2 & 2 & 1 & -1 & 10 \\
   &   & -4 & 6 & -10 \\
\hline
   & 2 & -3 & 5 & 0
\end{array}
$$

2.

$$
\begin{array}{r|rrrr}
4 & 3 & -10 & 0 & -5 \\
  &   & 12 & 8 & 32 \\
\hline
  & 3 & 2 & 8 & 27
\end{array}
$$

Divide using polynomial long division.

3. $(x^2 - 6x + 10) \div (x - 1)$

4. $(x^2 + 2x - 11) \div (x + 2)$

5. $(x^2 + 3x - 18) \div (x + 6)$

6. $(x^2 + 3x - 6) \div (x + 5)$

7. $(4x^2 - 7x - 4) \div (x - 4)$

8. $(2x^2 - x + 5) \div (x + 3)$

9. $(x^2 + 4) \div (x - 2)$

10. $(x^3 + 11x^2 + 25x - 21) \div (x + 7)$

Divide using synthetic division.

11. $(x^2 + 8x - 9) \div (x + 9)$

12. $(x^2 - x - 1) \div (x + 1)$

13. $(x^2 + 3x - 10) \div (x - 2)$

14. $(x^2 - 6x + 4) \div (x + 3)$

15. $(x^2 + 5x - 7) \div (x + 4)$

16. $(2x^2 - 7x - 15) \div (x - 5)$

17. $(x^3 + x + 2) \div (x - 1)$

18. $(x^2 - 7) \div (x + 2)$

You are given an expression for the area of the rectangle. Find an expression for the missing dimension.

19. $A = x^2 + 10x + 21$

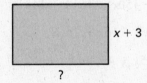

20. $A = x^2 + 2x - 8$

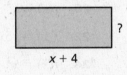

21. $A = x^2 + 8x + 15$

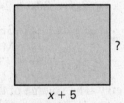

22. Publishing The profit P (in thousands of dollars) for an educational publisher can be modeled by $P = -b^3 + 5b^2 + b$ where b is the number of workbooks printed (in thousands). Currently, the publisher prints 5000 workbooks and makes a profit of $5000. What lesser number of workbooks could the publisher print and still yield the same profit?

Name _____ Date _____

Practice B

For use with pages 362–368

Divide using polynomial long division.

1. $(x^2 + 5x - 14) \div (x - 2)$

2. $(x^2 - 2x - 48) \div (x + 5)$

3. $(x^3 + x + 30) \div (x + 3)$

4. $(6x^2 - 5x + 9) \div (2x - 1)$

5. $(8x^3 + 5x^2 - 12x + 10) \div (x^2 - 3)$

6. $(5x^4 + 2x^3 - 9x + 12) \div (x^2 - 3x + 4)$

Divide using synthetic division.

7. $(x^2 + 7x + 12) \div (x + 4)$

8. $(x^3 - 3x^2 + 8x - 5) \div (x - 1)$

9. $(x^4 - 7x^2 + 9x - 10) \div (x - 2)$

10. $(2x^4 - x^3 + 4) \div (x + 1)$

11. $(2x^4 - 11x^3 + 15x^2 + 6x - 18) \div (x - 3)$

12. $(x^4 - 6x^3 - 40x + 33) \div (x - 7)$

A polynomial f and a factor of f are given. Factor f completely.

13. $f(x) = x^3 - 3x^2 - 16x - 12;\ x - 6$

14. $f(x) = x^3 - 12x^2 + 12x + 80;\ x - 10$

15. $f(x) = x^3 - 18x^2 + 95x - 126;\ x - 9$

16. $f(x) = x^3 - x^2 - 21x + 45;\ x + 5$

17. $f(x) = 4x^3 - 4x^2 - 9x + 9;\ x - 1$

18. $f(x) = 3x^3 - 16x^2 - 103x + 36;\ x + 4$

A polynomial f and one zero of f are given. Find the other zeros of f.

19. $f(x) = x^3 + 2x^2 - 20x + 24;\ -6$

20. $f(x) = x^3 + 11x^2 - 150x - 1512;\ -14$

21. $f(x) = 2x^3 + 3x^2 - 39x - 20;\ 4$

22. $f(x) = 15x^3 - 119x^2 - 10x + 16;\ 8$

23. $f(x) = x^3 - 3x^2 - 45x + 175;\ -7$

24. $f(x) = x^3 - 9x^2 - 5x + 45;\ 9$

25. **Geometry** The volume of the box shown at the right is given by $V = 2x^3 - 11x^2 + 10x + 8$. Find an expression for the missing dimension.

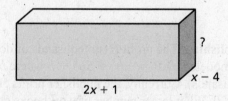

$?$

$x - 4$

$2x + 1$

26. **Fuel Consumption** From 1995 to 2002, the total fuel consumption T (in billions of gallons) by cars in the United States and the U.S. population P (in millions) can be modeled by

$$T = -0.003x^3 - 0.02x^2 + 1.3x + 68 \text{ and } P = 3x + 267$$

where x is the number of years since 1995. Write a function for the average amount of fuel consumed by each person from 1995 to 2002.

Name _____   Date _____

Practice C
For use with pages 362–368

Divide using polynomial long division.

1. $(4x^3 - 2x^2 + 6x - 1) \div (2x + 3)$

2. $(5x^4 + 8x - 9) \div (x^2 - 4)$

3. $(x^3 + 5) \div (2x^2 - 1)$

4. $(6x^4 - 9x^3 - 19x^2 + 31x - 5) \div (2x^2 + x - 5)$

5. $(2x^4 + 2x^3 - 10x - 9) \div (x^3 + x^2 - 5)$

6. $(8x^4 + 2x^2 - 12x + 9) \div (x^2 + x - 3)$

Divide using synthetic division.

7. $(2x^3 - 4x + 5) \div (x + 4)$

8. $(6x^3 - 7x) \div (x - 2)$

9. $(x^4 + 5x^3 - 2x^2 - 4x + 4) \div (x + 3)$

10. $(3x^4 - x^2 + 6x) \div (x - 3)$

11. $(4x + 2x^3 + 7x^2 - 1) \div (x + 1)$

12. $(2x^3 + 3x^5 + 1 - 5x) \div (x - 1)$

A polynomial f and a factor of f are given. Factor f completely.

13. $f(x) = x^3 + 9x^2 - 37x - 165; x - 5$

14. $f(x) = 4x^3 + 8x^2 - 25x - 50; x + 2$

15. $f(x) = x^4 - 4x^3 + 8x - 32; x - 4$

16. $f(x) = 4x^4 + 26x^3 - 8x^2 + 39x - 21; x + 7$

17. $f(x) = x^5 - 3x^4 - 4x^3 + x^2 - 3x - 4; x + 1$

18. $f(x) = 6x^5 - 38x^4 + 12x^3 - 15x^2 + 95x - 30; x - 6$

A polynomial f and one zero of f are given. Find the other zeros of f.

19. $f(x) = x^3 - 10x^2 - 3x + 108; 4$

20. $f(x) = 9x^3 + 45x^2 - 4x - 20; -5$

21. $f(x) = 12x^3 + 8x^2 - 13x + 3; \frac{1}{2}$

22. $f(x) = x^3 + x^2 - 13x + 3; 3$

23. $f(x) = 2x^3 + 11x^2 + 9x + 2; -\frac{1}{2}$

24. $f(x) = x^3 + x^2 + 2x + 24; -3$

25. **Company Profit** The price p (in dollars) that a television manufacturer is able to charge for a television is given by $p = 300 - 8x^2$ where x is the number (in millions) of televisions produced. It costs the company $175 to make a television.

   a. Write an expression for the company's total revenue in terms of x.

   b. Write a function for the company's profit P as a function of x.

   c. Currently, the company produces 2.5 million televisions and makes a profit of $187,500,000. Write and solve an equation to find a lesser number of televisions that the company could produce and still yield the same profit.

   d. Do all of the solutions in part (c) make sense in this situation? *Explain.*

Study Guide

LESSON 5.5

For use with pages 362–368

GOAL Use theorems to factor polynomials.

Vocabulary

Polynomial long division can be used to divide a polynomial $f(x)$ by a divisor polynomial $d(x)$, producing a quotient polynomial $q(x)$ and a remainder polynomial $r(x)$.

Synthetic division can be used to divide any polynomial by a divisor of the form $x - k$.

EXAMPLE 1 ## Use polynomial long division

Divide $f(x) = x^4 + 1$ by $x + 1$, using long division.

Solution

$$
\begin{array}{r}
x^3 - x^2 + x - 1 \\
x + 1 \overline{\smash{\big)}\, x^4 + 0x^3 + 0x^2 + 0x + 1}
\end{array}
$$

$\underline{x^4 + x^3}$	Multiply divisor by $x^4/x = x^3$.
$-x^3 + 0x^2$	Subtract.
$\underline{-x^3 - x^2}$	Multiply divisor by $-x^3/x = -x^2$.
$x^2 + 0x$	Subtract.
$\underline{-x^2 - x}$	Multiply divisor by $x^2/x = x$.
$-x + 1$	Subtract.
$\underline{x + 1}$	Multiply divisor by $-x/x = -1$.
2	Subtract.

$$\frac{x^4 + 1}{x + 1} = x^3 - x^2 + x - 1 + \frac{2}{x + 1}$$

EXAMPLE 2 ## Use synthetic division

Divide $f(x) = x^4 + 1$ by $x + 1$, using synthetic division.

Solution

$$
\begin{array}{r|rrrrr}
-1 & 1 & 0 & 0 & 0 & 1 \\
   &   & -1 & 1 & -1 & 1 \\
\hline
   & 1 & -1 & 1 & -1 & 2
\end{array}
$$

coefficients of quotient ⟵ remainder

So, $\dfrac{x^4 + 1}{x + 1} = x^3 - x^2 + x - 1 + \dfrac{2}{x + 1}$, which is the same result as in Example 1.

Study Guide *continued*
For use with pages 362–368

Exercises for Examples 1 and 2

Divide using polynomial long division.

1. $(2x^4 + 2x^3 + x^2 - x - 1) \div (x^2 - x - 1)$

2. $(x^3 + 3x^2 - x - 3) \div (x^2 - 1)$

Divide using synthetic division.

3. $(x^4 + 2x^3 - 5x^2 + 3x - 1) \div (x - 1)$

4. $(-x^4 + 4x^2 + 5x + 5) \div (x + 2)$

EXAMPLE 3 **Factor a polynomial**

Factor $f(x) = x^3 - 4x^2 + x + 6$ completely given that $x - 3$ is a factor.

Because $x - 3$ is a factor of $f(x)$, you know that $f(3) = 0$. Use synthetic division to find the other factors.

$$
\begin{array}{r|rrrr}
3 & 1 & -4 & 1 & 6 \\
  &   & 3 & -3 & -6 \\
\hline
  & 1 & -1 & -2 & 0
\end{array}
$$

Use the result to write $f(x)$ as a product of two factors and then factor completely.

$f(x) = x^3 - 4x^2 + x + 6 = (x - 3)(x^2 - x - 2) = (x - 3)(x - 2)(x + 1)$

Exercises for Example 3

Factor the polynomial completely given that $x - 3$ is a factor.

5. $x^3 - 3x^2 - x + 3$ 6. $x^3 - 2x^2 - 5x + 6$ 7. $x^3 - 6x^2 + 11x - 6$

EXAMPLE 4 **Finding zeros of equations**

Find the other zeros of $f(x) = x^3 + 2x^2 - x - 2$ given that $f(-1) = 0$.

Because $f(-1) = 0$, $x + 1$ is a factor of f. Use synthetic division.

$$
\begin{array}{r|rrrr}
-1 & 1 & 2 & -1 & -2 \\
   &   & 1 & -1 & 2 \\
\hline
   & 1 & 1 & -2 & 0
\end{array}
$$

Use the result to write $f(x)$ as a product of two factors and then factor completely.

$f(x) = x^3 + 2x^2 - x - 2$

$\quad = (x + 1)(x^2 + x - 2)$

$\quad = (x + 1)(x + 2)(x - 1)$

The zeros are -1, -2, and 1.

Exercises for Example 4

A polynomial f and one zero of f are given. Find the other zeros of f.

8. $f(x) = x^3 - 3x^2 + 4; x = 2$ 9. $f(x) = x^3 - x^2 - 4x + 4; x = -2$

LESSON 5.5 Quick Catch-Up for Absent Students

For use with pages 362–369

The items checked below were covered in class on (date missed) _____

Lesson 5.5: Apply the Remainder and Factor Theorems

_____ **Goal:** Use theorems to factor polynomials. (pp. 362–365)

Material Covered:

_____ Example 1: Use polynomial long division

_____ Avoid errors

_____ Example 2: Use polynomial long division with a linear divisor

_____ Guided Practice for Examples 1 and 2

_____ Example 3: Use synthetic division

_____ Divide polynomials

_____ Example 4: Factor a polynomial

_____ Avoid errors

_____ Guided Practice for Examples 3 and 4

_____ Example 5: Standardized Test Practice

_____ Example 6: Use a polynomial model

_____ Guided Practice for Examples 5 and 6

Vocabulary:

polynomial long division, p. 362
synthetic division, p. 363

_____ Other (specify)

_____

Homework and Additional Learning Support

_____ Textbook (specify) pp. 366–368

_____

_____ *Study Guide* worksheet (specify exercises)_____

_____ @*HomeTutor* for Lesson 5.5

_____ Mixed Review of Problem Solving 5.1–5.5 (p. 369)

Problem Solving Workshop: Mixed Problem Solving

For use with pages 330–368

1. **Multi-Step Problem** On February 17, 1998, *Voyager I* became the most distant manmade object in space at a distance of 10,400,000,000 kilometers from Earth.

   a. Write the distance in scientific notation.

   b. *Voyager I* traveled an average of 1.39×10^6 kilometers per day. How long did it take *Voyager I* to travel this distance?

2. **Multi-Step Problem** You are designing a rectangular wooden box with width 4 inches greater than its height and length 3 times its height. The box has wood that is 1 inch thick on each of the four sides and on the top and bottom.

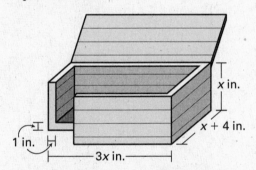

   x in.

   x + 4 in.

   1 in.

   3x in.

   a. Write a polynomial function $O(x)$ in standard form for the volume of the rectangular prism formed by the outer surfaces of the box.

   b. Write a polynomial function $I(x)$ in standard form for the volume of the inside of the box.

   c. Let $W(x)$ be a polynomial function for the volume of the wood. How is $W(x)$ related to $O(x)$ and $I(x)$?

   d. Write $W(x)$ in standard form. What is the volume of the wood when $x = 6$ inches?

3. **Open-Ended** Write a polynomial function that has degree 5 and end behavior given by $f(x) \to +\infty$ as $x \to -\infty$ and $f(x) \to -\infty$ as $x \to +\infty$. Then graph the function to check your answer.

4. **Gridded Answer** A gift box has a volume of 450 cubic inches. The width of the box is 4 inches less than the length. The height is twice the width. What is the width in inches of the gift box?

5. **Extended Response** From 1992 to 2002, the number of bachelor degrees B in the field of engineering can be modeled by $B = 4.3t^4 - 49.6t^3 - 34t^2 + 836.6t + 61,181$ where t is the number of years since 1992.

   a. Classify the function by degree and type.

   b. Make a table of values for the function.

   c. Sketch a graph of the function and describe the end behavior. According to the function, would you expect the number of bachelor degrees in 2012 to be more than or less than the number in 2002? *Explain.*

6. **Short Response** The radius of the sun is 6.96×10^5 kilometers. The radius of Pluto is 1.195×10^3 kilometers. Assume the sun and Pluto are spheres. *Compare* the surface area of the sun with the surface area of Pluto.

7. **Extended Response** The price p (in dollars) that a manufacturer charges for a DVD player is given by $p = 120 - 12x^2$ where x is the number (in millions) of DVD players produced. It costs the company $24 to make a DVD player. The company produces 1 million DVD players and makes a profit of $84,000,000.

   a. Write a function that gives the total revenue R in terms of x.

   b. Write a function that gives the company's profit P in terms of x.

   c. Write and solve an equation to find other values of x that yield a profit of $84,000,000.

   d. Do all the solutions in part (c) make sense in this situation? *Explain.*

LESSONS 5.5 & 5.9 Problem Solving Workshop: Gridded Answer Sheet

For use with Mixed Problem Solving for 5.1–5.5 and 5.6–5.9

Challenge Practice
For use with pages 362–368

1. Show that $(x - 2)$ and $(x + 3)$ are factors of $f(x) = 2x^4 + 7x^3 - 4x^2 - 27x - 18$.
Then find the remaining factors of $f(x)$.

2. Show that $(x + 2)$ and $(x - 4)$ are factors of $f(x) = 8x^4 - 14x^3 - 71x^2 - 10x + 24$.
Then find the remaining factors of $f(x)$.

3. Show that $(x - 1)$ and $(x + 7)$ are factors of $f(x) = 2x^4 + x^3 - 75x^2 + 107x - 35$.
Then find the remaining factors of $f(x)$.

4. Show that $(x + 8)$ and $(x - 6)$ are factors of $f(x) = 12x^4 + 19x^3 - 588x^2 + 236x + 96$.
Then find the remaining factors of $f(x)$.

In Exercises 5 and 6, find the value of k such that the denominator divides evenly into the numerator.

5. $\dfrac{x^3 + 4x^2 - 3x + k}{x - 5}$

6. $\dfrac{x^5 - 2x^2 + x + k}{x + 2}$

In Exercises 7 and 8, perform the division. Assume that n is a positive integer.

7. $\left(x^{3n} + 9x^{2n} + 27x^n + 27\right) \div \left(x^n + 3\right)$

8. $\left(x^{3n} - 3x^{2n} + 5x^n - 6\right) \div \left(x^n - 2\right)$

9. Complete each polynomial division.
  a. $\left(x^2 - 1\right) \div \left(x - 1\right)$
  b. $\left(x^3 - 1\right) \div \left(x - 1\right)$
  c. $\left(x^4 - 1\right) \div \left(x - 1\right)$

10. Use the results of Exercise 9 to find a formula for the polynomial division
$\left(x^n - 1\right) \div \left(x - 1\right)$.

11. Use the formula for polynomial division to prove the remainder theorem.

12. Use the formula for polynomial division and the remainder theorem to prove the
factor theorem. (*Hint:* You must first prove that if a polynomial $f(x)$ has a factor
$(x - k)$, then $f(k) = 0$. Then you must prove that if $f(k) = 0$, then the polynomial
$f(x)$ has a factor of $(x - k)$.)

LESSON 5.6 Teaching Guide

Key Concept

The rational zero theorem can be used to list the possible rational zeros of functions. You will find actual zeros in polynomials by testing the possible rational zeros using synthetic division and sketching the graph of the function to help choose values of zero to test.

Teaching the Lesson

Differentiating Instruction: See the Teacher's Edition side column notes on page 371 and the notes on differentiating instruction in the *Algebra 2 Toolkit*.

Teaching Notes and Suggested Questions: See the Teacher's Edition side columns on pages 370–373.

Activity Generator: See the Activity Generator Support Manual.

Animated Algebra: You may want to include the animation on page 371 in your lesson.

Starting the Lesson

Connect to Prior Learning Be sure that students recall the following ideas:

- solving quadratic equations (p. 252 and p. 259)

- leading coefficient (p. 337)

Alternative Lesson Starter

We use *zero* to refer to many things, such as the number zero, the origin on the number line, the identity element for addition, and a positional placeholder. But where did the word *zero* come from? Actually it evolved over centuries. The Hindus used the word *sunya*, meaning empty or void. The Arabs translated this into *sifr*. Later it was translated into the Latin word *Zephirum*. This becomes *zeuero* in Italian, resembling the word *zero*.

Questions to Start the Lesson

1. What is the degree and the leading coefficient of the equation $7x^2 + 20x - 3 = 0$? Can the left hand side of this equation be factored? What are the factors?

2. What property allows you to set an equation's factors to zero to solve for the roots?

3. Why are the x-intercepts of a function also called the zeros of a function? What are the zeros of the equation above?

4. Can all equations be easily factored? What other ways can you solve quadratic equations?

Common Student Errors

- Not eliminating duplicates when finding rational zeros

  Tip Remind students to make sure to eliminate duplicates such as $\frac{7}{5}$ and $\frac{14}{10}$.

- Not using the quotient polynomial from the synthetic division to continue searching for zeros

  Tip Remind students that each time they find a zero of the polynomial function, they must rewrite the original function as a product of a binomial and another polynomial. This new polynomial is the quotient from the synthetic division, which is the polynomial they must use to continue searching for zeros, *not the original function*.

Teaching Strategy of the Day

Student Preparation Provide a test review time before each test. Outline the goals or skills to be covered in the test. Prepare sample questions to use during the review.

LESSON 5.6

LESSON 5.6	**Lesson Plan** continued

Standard Schedule: 2 day lesson   Block Schedule: 0.5 day lesson with 5.5, and 0.5 day with 5.7

GOAL **Find all real zeros of a polynomial function.**

State Standards _____

Focus and Motivate

Starting Options
_____Homework Check (5.5): TE p. 366; Answer Transparencies
_____Daily Homework Quiz (5.5): TE p. 368
_____Warm-Up: TE p. 370 or Transparencies
_____Starting the Lesson Questions: Teaching Guide
_____Motivating the Lesson: TE p. 371

Teach

Teaching Options
_____Essential Question: TE p. 370
_____Alternative Lesson Openers: Electronic Classroom
_____Classroom Activity: Activity Generator; Chapter Resource Book p. 60
_____Examples 1–4: PE pp. 370–373
_____Extra Examples 1–4 with Key Questions: TE pp. 371–373
_____Problem Solving Workshop: Using Alternative Methods:
Chapter Resource Book p. 67
_____Notetaking Guide pp. 147–149

Checking for Understanding
_____Closing the Lesson: TE p. 373
_____Guided Practice Exercises: PE pp. 371–373

Practice and Apply

Assigning Homework
_____Basic: Day 1: EP pp. 1013 Exs. 45–48; pp. 374–377 Exs. 1–18, 52–61;
Day 2: pp. 374–377 Exs. 19–29, 45–49, 62–67
_____Average: Day 1: pp. 374–377 Exs. 1, 2, 4–10, 12–18, 36–38, 52–61;
Day 2: pp. 374–377 Exs. 21–23, 27–32, 39, 40, 45–50, 62–67
_____Advanced: Day 1: pp. 374–377 Exs. 1, 2, 5–10, 13–18, 36–39, 52–61;
Day 2: pp. 374–377 Exs. 23, 30–44*, 46–51*, 62–67
_____Block: pp. 374–377 Exs. 1, 2, 4–10, 12–18, 36–38, 52–61 (with 5.5);
pp. 374–377 Exs. 21–23, 27–32, 39, 40, 45–50, 62–67 (with 5.7)
_____Practice Masters: Chapter Resource Book pp. 61–63 (Levels A, B, or C)

Assess and Reteach

Differentiating Instruction
_____Study Guide: Chapter Resource Book pp. 64–65
_____Tutorial Software
_____Challenge: Chapter Resource Book p. 68
_____Remediation and Intervention Package: _____
_____English Language Learners Package: _____

Preparing for Standardized Tests
_____Standardized Test Practice: PE pp. 374–376 Exs. 2, 23, 38, 39, 40, 50

Assessing the Lesson
_____Daily Homework Quiz (5.6): TE p. 377 or Transparencies

LESSON 5.6

LESSON 5.6 Spreadsheet Keystrokes

For use with Spreadsheet Activity 5.6 on page 378

EXCEL

STEP 2

Select cell A1.

x `ENTER`

Select cell A2.

−5.0 `ENTER`

Select cell A3.

= A2 + 0.1 `ENTER`

Select cells A3–A102.

From the **Edit** menu, choose **Fill**, then **Down**.

STEP 3

Select cell B1.

f(x) `ENTER`

Select cell B2.

= 6*A2^3 + 11*A2^2 − 19*A2 + 6 `ENTER`

Select cells B2–B102.

From the **Edit** menu, choose **Fill**, then **Down**.

LESSON 5.6

LESSON 5.6 Practice A
For use with pages 370–378

1. Can you use the rational zero theorem to find the zeros of the polynomial function $f(x) = 0.4x^2 - 3x + 2.2$? Explain why or why not.

List the possible rational zeros of the function using the rational zero theorem.

2. $f(x) = x^3 - 5x + 16$

3. $g(x) = x^4 + 8x^2 - 18$

4. $h(x) = x^5 + 2x^4 - 3x - 24$

5. $f(x) = x^8 - 2x^5 + x^4 - 3x + 20$

6. $h(x) = 2x^3 - 5x^2 - 9$

7. $g(x) = 3x^3 + 7x + 12$

Use synthetic division to decide which of the following are zeros of the function: −3, −1, 1, 3.

8. $f(x) = x^3 - 9x + 3$

9. $g(x) = x^4 + 3x^3 - 7x^2 - 27x - 18$

10. $g(x) = 2x^4 - 9x^3 + 8x^2 + 9x - 10$

11. $h(x) = 3x^4 + 5x^2 - 17x + 9$

Find all rational zeros of the function.

12. $f(x) = x^3 + x^2 - 14x - 24$

13. $f(x) = x^3 - 2x^2 - x + 2$

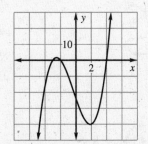

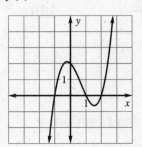

Find all real zeros of the function.

14. $f(x) = x^3 - 8x^2 - 23x + 30$

15. $g(x) = x^3 + 2x^2 - 11x - 12$

16. $h(x) = x^3 - 7x^2 + 2x + 40$

17. $h(x) = x^3 + 9x^2 - 4x - 36$

18. $g(x) = x^4 - 5x^3 + 7x^2 + 3x - 10$

19. $f(x) = x^4 - 2x^3 - 7x^2 + 8x + 12$

20. $f(x) = x^4 + 3x^3 - 21x^2 - 43x + 60$

21. $g(x) = x^4 + x^3 - 11x^2 - 9x + 18$

22. Crafts You have 18 cubic inches of wax, and you want to make a candle in the shape of a pyramid with a square base.

a. Write an equation that shows that the volume of the candle is 18 cubic inches.

b. Use the rational zero theorem to list all possible rational zeros of the equation in part (a).

c. Find all real values of x that are valid as a dimension of the candle.

d. Find the dimensions of the candle.

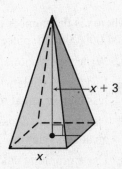

LESSON 5.6 **Practice B**
For use with pages 370–378

List the possible rational zeros of the function using the rational zero theorem.

1. $f(x) = x^4 - 6x^3 + 8x^2 - 21$ 2. $h(x) = 2x^3 + 7x^2 - 7x + 30$

3. $h(x) = 5x^4 + 12x^3 - 16x^2 + 10$ 4. $g(x) = 9x^5 + 3x^3 + 7x - 4$

Find all real zeros of the function.

5. $f(x) = x^3 - 3x^2 - 6x + 8$ 6. $g(x) = x^3 + 4x^2 - x - 4$

7. $h(x) = x^3 + 4x^2 + x - 6$ 8. $g(x) = x^3 + 5x^2 - x - 5$

9. $f(x) = x^3 + 72 - 5x^2 - 18x$ 10. $f(x) = x^3 + x^2 - 2x - 2$

Use the graph to shorten the list of possible rational zeros of the function. Then find all real zeros of the function.

11. $f(x) = 4x^3 - 8x^2 - 15x + 9$ 12. $f(x) = 2x^3 - 5x^2 - 4x + 10$

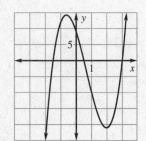   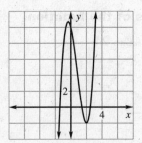

Find all real zeros of the function.

13. $g(x) = 2x^3 + 4x^2 - 2x - 4$ 14. $f(x) = 2x^3 - 5x^2 - 14x + 8$

15. $h(x) = 8x^3 - 6x^2 - 23x + 6$ 16. $g(x) = 2x^4 + x^3 - x^2 - x - 1$

17. $h(x) = 2x^4 + 5x^3 - 5x^2 - 5x + 3$ 18. $f(x) = 2x^4 + 3x^3 - 6x^2 - 6x + 4$

19. **Mail** From 1995 to 2003, the amount of mail M (in billions of pieces) handled by the U.S. Postal Service can be modeled by

$$M = 0.05(t^4 - 18t^3 + 89t^2 - 32t + 3680)$$

where t is the number of years since 1995. In which year was there about 204,000,000,000 pieces of mail handled?

a. Write a polynomial equation that can be used to answer the question.

b. List the possible whole-number solutions of the equation in part (a) that are less than or equal to 8.

c. Use synthetic division to determine which of the possible solutions in part (b) is an actual solution. Then answer the question in the problem statement.

d. Use a graphing calculator to graph and identify any additional real solutions of the equation that are reasonable.

Practice C
For use with pages 370–378

Find all real zeros of the function.

1. $f(x) = x^3 - 4x^2 - 7x + 10$

2. $g(x) = x^5 - x^4 - 7x^3 + 11x^2 - 8x + 12$

3. $h(x) = x^4 + 4x^3 + x^2 - 8x - 6$

4. $g(x) = x^3 + 2x^2 - 34x + 7$

5. $f(x) = x^4 + 4x^3 - 14x^2 - 20x - 3$

6. $h(x) = x^5 + 15x^4 + 72x^3 + 80x^2 - 225x - 375$

7. $f(x) = 2x^4 + 5x^3 - 6x^2 - 7x + 6$

8. $g(x) = 6x^4 + 35x^3 + 35x^2 - 55x - 21$

9. $h(x) = 24x^4 - 26x^3 - 45x^2 - x + 6$

10. $f(x) = 8x^3 + 28x^2 + 14x - 15$

11. $g(x) = 6x^4 + 25x^3 + 32x^2 + 15x + 2$

12. $h(x) = 12x^4 + 28x^3 - 11x^2 - 13x + 5$

13. $f(x) = 18x^5 + 51x^4 - 60x + 75 - 34x^3 - 178x^2$

14. $g(x) = 6x^5 - 116x^3 - x^4 - 53x^2 + 24 + 50x$

15. Write a polynomial function f that has a leading coefficient of 6 and has 12 possible rational zeros according to the rational zero theorem.

16. **Critical Thinking** Consider the function $f(x) = 2x^4 + 5x^3 - 21x^2 - 36x$.
    a. Explain why the rational zero theorem cannot be directly applied to this function.
    b. Factor out the common monomial factor of f.
    c. Apply the rational zero theorem to find all the real zeros of f.
    d. Find all the real zeros of $f(x) = 3x^5 - x^4 - 6x^3 + 2x^2$.

17. **Critical Thinking** Consider the functions
    $f(x) = x^3 + 2x^2 - 19x - 20$, $g(x) = -x^2 - 2x^2 + 19x + 20$,
    $h(x) = 2x^3 + 4x^2 - 38x - 40$, and $j(x) = 4x^3 + 8x^2 - 76x - 80$.
    a. Use the rational zero theorem to find all of the real zeros of each function.
    b. Note that $g(x) = -f(x)$, $h(x) = 2f(x)$, and $j(x) = 4f(x)$.
       What can you conclude about the zeros of $f(x)$ and $af(x)$?
    c. Explain why the rational zero theorem cannot be directly applied to
       $$f(x) = \frac{4}{3}x^3 + 3x^2 - \frac{10}{3}x - 1.$$
    d. Use the conclusion from part (b) to find the real zeros of the function in part (c).

LESSON 5.6 Study Guide
For use with pages 370–378

GOAL **Find all real zeros of a polynomial function.**

EXAMPLE 1 **Find zeros when the leading coefficient is 1**

Find all real zeros of $f(x) = x^3 - 7x^2 + 14x - 8$.

The Rational Zero Theorem states if $a_n x^n + \cdots + a_1 x + a_0$ has integer coefficients, then every rational zero of f has the form $\dfrac{p}{q} = \dfrac{\text{factor of constant term } a_0}{\text{factor of leading coefficient } a_n}$.

STEP 1 **List** the possible rational zeros. The leading coefficient is 1 and the constant term is -8. The possible rational zeros are: $x = \pm 1, \pm 2, \pm 4, \pm 8$

STEP 2 **Test** these zeros using synthetic division.

Test $x = 4$:

$$
\begin{array}{r|rrrr}
4 & 1 & -7 & 14 & -8 \\
  &   & 4 & -12 & 8 \\
\hline
  & 1 & -3 & 2 & 0
\end{array} \longleftarrow \text{4 is a zero.}
$$

Because 4 is a zero of f, write $f(x) = (x - 4)(x^2 - 3x + 2)$.

STEP 3 **Factor** the trinomial and use the factor theorem.

$$f(x) = (x - 4)(x^2 - 3x + 2) = (x - 4)(x - 2)(x - 1)$$

The zeros are 1, 2, and 4.

EXAMPLE 2 **Find zeros when the leading coefficient is not 1**

Find all real zeros of $3x^3 - 17x^2 + 18x + 8$.

STEP 1 **List** the possible rational zeros of f: $x = \pm 1, \pm 2, \pm 4, \pm \dfrac{1}{3}, \pm \dfrac{2}{3}, \pm \dfrac{4}{3}$

STEP 2 **Choose** a reasonable value to check using the graph of the function.

STEP 3 **Check** $x = -\dfrac{1}{3}$:

$$
\begin{array}{r|rrrr}
-\frac{1}{3} & 3 & -17 & 18 & 8 \\
  &   & -1 & 6 & -8 \\
\hline
  & 3 & -18 & 24 & 0
\end{array} \longleftarrow -\dfrac{1}{3} \text{ is a zero.}
$$

STEP 4 **Factor** out a binomial using the result of synthetic division.

$$f(x) = \left(x + \frac{1}{3}\right)(3x^2 - 18x + 24) = \left(x + \frac{1}{3}\right)(3)(x^2 - 6x + 8)$$

$$= (3x + 1)(x - 2)(x - 4)$$

The real zeros of f are $-\dfrac{1}{3}$, 2, and 4.

Study Guide *continued*

Exercises for Examples 1 and 2

Find all real zeros of the function.

1. $x^3 + x^2 - 4x - 4$ **2.** $x^3 + 2x^2 - 11x - 12$ **3.** $2x^3 - 5x^2 + x + 2$

4. $x^3 - 3x^2 - x + 3$ **5.** $x^3 - 2x^2 - 5x + 6$ **6.** $x^3 - 6x^2 + 11x - 6$

EXAMPLE 3 ## Solve a multi-step problem

Desk Organizer The length of a desk organizer is 4 inches greater than the width. The height is $\frac{1}{3}$ of the width and the volume is 21 cubic inches. What are the dimensions of the organizer?

STEP 1 **Write** an equation for the volume of the organizer.

Volume (cubic inches)	=	Height (inches)	·	Height (inches)	·	Width (inches)
21	=	$\frac{1}{3}x$	·	$(x + 4)$	·	x

$63 = x^3 + 4x^2$ Multiply each side by 3 and simplify.

$0 = x^3 + 4x^2 - 63$ Subtract 63 from each side.

STEP 2 **Find** the possible rational solutions: $\pm 1, \pm 3, \pm 7, \pm 9, \pm 21, \pm 63$

STEP 3 **Test** the possible rational solutions. Only positive x-values make sense.

$$
\begin{array}{r|rrrr}
3 & 1 & 4 & 0 & -63 \\
  &   & 3 & 21 & 63 \\
\hline
  & 1 & 7 & 21 & 0
\end{array}
$$

3 is a solution.

STEP 4 **Check** for other solutions. The other solutions are imaginary and can be discarded.

The width is 3 inches, the length is $3 + 4 = 7$ inches and the height is 1 inch.

Exercises for Example 3

7. A pyramid has a square base with sides of length x, a height of $x - 2$, and a volume of 3. Write a polynomial equation to model the situation. List the possible rational solutions of the equation, and then find the dimensions of the pyramid.

8. A rectangular prism has sides of lengths x, $\frac{1}{2}x$, and $x - 1$, and a volume of 24 cubic inches. Write a polynomial equation to model the situation. List the possible rational solutions of the equation, and then find the dimensions of the prism.

LESSON 5.6 Quick Catch-Up for Absent Students

For use with pages 370–378

The items checked below were covered in class on (date missed) _____

Lesson 5.6: Find Rational Zeros

_____ **Goal:** Find all real zeros of a polynomial function. (pp. 370–373)

Material Covered:

    _____ Example 1: List possible rational zeros

    _____ Avoid errors

    _____ Guided Practice for Example 1

    _____ Example 2: Find zeros when the leading coefficient is 1

    _____ Avoid errors

    _____ Guided Practice for Example 2

    _____ Example 3: Find zeros when the leading coefficient is not 1

    _____ Guided Practice for Example 3

    _____ Example 4: Solve a multi-step problem

    _____ Guided Practice for Example 4

_____ Other (specify)

_____

Homework and Additional Learning Support

_____ Textbook (specify) pp. 374–377

_____

_____ *Study Guide* worksheet (specify exercises)_____

_____ *@HomeTutor* for Lesson 5.6

Activity 5.6: Use the Location Principle

_____ **Goal:** Use the location principle to identify zeros of a polynomial function. (p. 378)

LESSON 5.6 Problem Solving Workshop: Using Alternative Methods

For use with pages 370–378

Another Way to Solve Example 4 on page 373

Multiple Representations In Example 4 on page 373, you saw how to solve a problem about an ice sculpture by finding zeros. You can also solve the problem by *using a graph*.

PROBLEM **Ice Sculptures** Some ice sculptures are made by filling a mold with water and then freezing it. You are making such an ice sculpture for a school dance. It is to be shaped like a pyramid with a height that is 1 foot greater than the length of each side of its square base. The volume of the ice sculpture is 4 cubic feet. What are the dimensions of the mold?

METHOD **Using a graph** You can solve the problem by using a graph.

STEP 1 **Write** an equation for the volume of the ice sculpture.

$$\boxed{\begin{array}{c}\text{Volume}\\ \text{(cubic feet)}\end{array}} = \frac{1}{3} \cdot \boxed{\begin{array}{c}\text{Area of base}\\ \text{(square feet)}\end{array}} \cdot \boxed{\begin{array}{c}\text{Height}\\ \text{(feet)}\end{array}}$$

$$4 = \frac{1}{3} \cdot x^2 \cdot (x+1)$$

$$12 = x^3 + x^2 \qquad \text{Multiply each side by 3 and simplify.}$$

$$0 = x^3 + x^2 - 12 \qquad \text{Subtract 12 from each side.}$$

STEP 2 **Graph** the function using a graphing calculator and determine where the graph crosses the *x*-axis.

Because the function is odd with a positive leading coefficient, as $x \to -\infty, f(x) \to -\infty$ and as $x \to +\infty, f(x) \to +\infty$. The zero of the function occurs at $x = 2$.

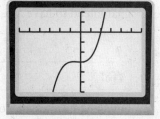

The base of the mold is 2 feet by 2 feet and the height of the mold is 3 feet.

PRACTICE

1. **Candle** You are designing a cone-shaped candle with a volume of 8π cubic inches. The height of the cone is 2 inches longer than the diameter of the base. What should be the diameter and height of the cone?

2. **Sand Castle** You want to design a sand castle mold to be a pyramid that will hold 144 cubic inches of sand. The height of the pyramid is 6 inches greater than the length of each side of its square base. What are the dimensions of the pyramid?

3. **What If?** You want to make a smaller pyramid with the same base and a height that is 2 inches greater than the length of each side of the base with a volume of 96 cubic inches. What are the dimensions of the pyramid?

4. **Wheelchair Ramp** The width of a concrete wheelchair ramp is 3 times the height and the length is 3 feet more than 8 times the height. The ramp uses 228 cubic feet of concrete. What are the dimensions of the ramp?

LESSON 5.6 # Challenge Practice

For use with pages 370–378

In Exercises 1–3, use the following information.

The following theorem, called the *intermediate value theorem*, can help you locate real zeros of a polynomial function.

Intermediate Value Theorem

Let a and b be real numbers such that $a < b$. If f is a polynomial function such that $f(a) \neq f(b)$, then in the interval $a \leq x \leq b$, f takes on every value between $f(a)$ and $f(b)$.

In other words, if you can find a value $x = a$ at which a polynomial function f is positive, and another value $x = b$ at which it is negative, you can conclude that the function has at least one real zero between these two values.

1. Create a table for the polynomial function showing the value of the polynomial for integer values of x between -5 and 5. Use the intermediate value theorem to determine intervals one unit in length in which the polynomial function is guaranteed to have a zero.

   a. $f(x) = x^3 - 3x^2 + 3$

   b. $f(x) = 3x^4 + 4x^3 - 3$

   c. $f(x) = 12x^3 - 32x^2 + 3x + 5$

   d. $f(x) = 2x^4 + 3x^3 - 2x^2 + 1$

2. Consider the function given by $f(x) = x^3 + x^2 + 1$.

   a. List the possible rational zeros of the function. Are these actual zeros of the function? *Explain* your reasoning.

   b. Copy and complete the table below. Use the intermediate value theorem to determine an interval one unit in length in which the polynomial function is guaranteed to have a zero.

x	-5	-4	-3	-2	-1	0	1	2	3	4	5
$f(x)$											

   c. Divide your interval from part (b) into tenths. Then evaluate the function at each value. Use the intermediate value theorem to determine an interval in which the polynomial function is guaranteed to have a zero.

   d. Repeat the process until you can approximate the zero to three decimal places.

3. **Manufacturing** The ordering and transportation costs C (in thousands of dollars) for the components used in manufacturing a product is given by

   $$C = 100\left(\frac{200}{x^2} + \frac{x}{x + 30}\right), x \geq 1$$

   where x is the order size (in hundreds). The related equation

   $3x^3 - 40x^2 - 2400x - 36,000 = 0$

   can be used to determine the order size that produces a minimum cost. Use the intermediate value theorem to determine an interval in which the optimal order size occurs.

LESSON 5.7 Teaching Guide

Key Concept

You will use the fundamental theorem of algebra to determine the number of solutions to a function. Then you will find the zeros of a polynomial function. You will use the zeros of a function to write a polynomial function that has rational coefficients and a leading coefficient of 1. Descartes' rule of signs will be used to determine the possible number of positive, negative, and imaginary zeros of a function. You will use a graphing calculator to approximate the real zeros of a function and of a polynomial model.

Teaching the Lesson

Differentiating Instruction: See the Teacher's Edition side column notes on page 382 and the notes on differentiating instruction in the *Algebra 2 Toolkit*.

Teaching Notes and Suggested Questions: See the Teacher's Edition side columns on pages 379–383.

Activity Generator: See the Activity Generator Support Manual.

Starting the Lesson

Motivate the Lesson Be sure that students recall the following ideas:

- complex conjugates (p. 278)

- the quadratic formula (p. 292)

- rational zero theorem (p. 370)

Alternative Lesson Starter

Carl F. Gauss was the first mathematician to complete the proof of the fundamental theorem of algebra. He also developed a theory explaining the distribution of an electric charge through the surface of an object. The theory became known as Gauss' Law and the standard unit of measurement of magnetic influence was later named the *gauss* in honor of his work.

Questions to Start the Lesson

1. In the previous section you used the rational zero theorem to list possible rational zeros of a function. What does the theorem state?

2. What are the possible rational zeros of the function $y = 2x^3 + 3x^2 - 8x + 16$?

3. What is the quadratic formula? How many and what type of solutions does the equation have when the discriminant is less than zero?

4. What is a complex conjugate? Find the product of $(5 - i\sqrt{6})$ and $(5 + i\sqrt{6})$.

Common Student Errors

- Assuming that stating the zeros of a polynomial function is enough to determine a unique answer

Tip Remind students why they are asked to find a function of *least degree with leading coefficient of 1*. Challenge students to find other polynomial functions with the same zeros.

Teaching Strategy of the Day

Asking Students Avoid negative reactions (facial expressions, body language, and so on) when a student gives a wrong answer. A student who has given an answer has tried. You want the student to be willing to continue to answer and ask questions during class.

LESSON 5.7

LESSON 5.7	**Lesson Plan** continued

Standard Schedule: 2 day lesson   Block Schedule: 0.5 day lesson with 5.6, and 0.5 day with 5.8

GOAL **Classify the zeros of polynomial functions.**

State Standards _____

Focus and Motivate

Starting Options
_____ Homework Check (5.6): TE p. 374; Answer Transparencies
_____ Daily Homework Quiz (5.6): TE p. 377
_____ Warm-Up: TE p. 379 or Transparencies
_____ Starting the Lesson Questions: Teaching Guide
_____ Motivating the Lesson: TE p. 380

Teach

Teaching Options
_____ Essential Question: TE p. 379
_____ Alternative Lesson Openers: Electronic Classroom
_____ Classroom Activity: Activity Generator; Chapter Resource Book p. 71
_____ Examples 1–6: PE pp. 379–383
_____ Extra Examples 1–6 with Key Questions: TE pp. 380--383
_____ Real-Life Application: Chapter Resource Book p. 80
_____ Notetaking Guide pp. 150–153

Checking for Understanding
_____ Closing the Lesson: TE p. 383
_____ Guided Practice Exercises: PE pp. 379–383

Practice and Apply

Assigning Homework
_____ Basic: Day 1: pp. 383–386 Exs. 1–6, 9–15, 20–27, 32, 33, 66–69;
Day 2: pp. 383–386 Exs. 35–49 odd, 59–63, 70–78
_____ Average: Day 1: pp. 383–386 Exs. 1, 2, 4–7, 9, 12–17, 22–29, 32, 33, 66–69;
Day 2: pp. 383–386 Exs. 34–50 even, 51–55, 61–64, 70–78 even
_____ Advanced: Day 1: pp. 383–386 Exs. 1, 2, 5–9, 14–19, 24–31, 33, 66–69;
Day 2: pp. 383–386 Exs. 38–41, 44–58*, 61–65*, 71–77 odd
_____ Block: pp. 383–386 Exs. 1, 2, 4–7, 9, 12–17, 22–29, 32, 33, 66–69 (with 5.6);
pp. 383–386 Exs. 34–50 even 51–55, 61–64, 70–78 even (with 5.8)
_____ Practice Masters: Chapter Resource Book pp. 74–76 (Levels A, B, or C)

Assess and Reteach

Differentiating Instruction
_____ Study Guide: Chapter Resource Book pp. 77–78
_____ Tutorial Software
_____ Challenge: Chapter Resource Book p. 81
_____ Remediation and Intervention Package: _____
_____ English Language Learners Package: _____

Preparing for Standardized Tests
_____ Standardized Test Practice: PE pp. 383–386 Exs. 2, 9, 33, 51, 52, 63, 64

Assessing the Lesson
_____ Daily Homework Quiz (5.7): TE p. 386 or Transparencies

Standardized Test *continued*
For use after Chapter 5

10. Which is *not* a possible rational solution of
$f(x) = 3x^3 - 11x^2 + 5x - 6$?

(A) $\pm\frac{1}{2}$ (B) $\pm\frac{2}{3}$

(C) ± 2 (D) ± 6

11. Based upon Descartes' Rule of Signs,
which of the following is the only possible
classification of the roots of the function
$u(k) = -3k^3 + 5k^2 - k + 4$?

(A) 3 positives, 0 negatives, 0 imaginary

(B) 0 positives, 3 negatives, 0 imaginary

(C) 1 positive, 1 negative, 1 imaginary

(D) 2 positives, 1 negative, 0 imaginary

12. What is (are) the local minimum value(s)
for $v(x) = 2x^3 - x^2 + 1$?

(A) 0   (B) $\frac{1}{3}$

(C) 0 and $\frac{1}{3}$ (D) There are none.

Gridded Answer

13. How many solutions does
$0 = -7m^3 - m^4 + 1$ have?

Short Response

14. A package has a length 10 inches greater
than its width and a height 12 inches less
than its width.

a. Determine the polynomial function
that will calculate the volume of a
package with width w.

b. To carry this package onto an
airplane, it cannot be larger than
4800 cubic inches. What should its
dimensions be if you want to have the
maximum allowable volume?

Extended Response

15. The number of students who use a college
math lab is tracked for several academic
years. The results are summarized in the
table below.

Year	1990	1991	1992	1993
Students	1287	1365	1402	1693

Year	1994	1995	1996	1997
Students	1952	1874	2021	2111

Year	1998	1999	2000	2001
Students	1994	1878	1763	1524

a. Let 1990 correspond to year $x = 0$,
1991 to year $x = 1$, and so on. Enter
the data into your graphing
calculator and make a scatter plot.
Which polynomial function does
it seem to model? Use polynomial
regression to obtain a model. Round
to two decimal places. What is the
regression equation you obtained?

b. Graph the model and predict what the
number of students will be in 2006.

c. Graph $y = 500$ in the same
viewing window. Find the
intersection point(s). Explain the
significance of your results.

LESSON 5.7

Investigating Algebra Activity:
Zeros of a Polynomial Function *continued*

For use before Lesson 5.7

TI-83 Plus

STEP 1

| Y= | X,T,θ,n | x^2 | + | 2 | X,T,θ,n | − | 8 |

| ENTER |

STEP 2

| ZOOM | 6

Casio CFX-9850GC Plus

STEP 1

From the main menu, choose GRAPH.

| X,θ,T | x^2 | + | 2 | X,θ,T | − | 8 | EXE |

STEP 2

| SHIFT | F3 | F3 | EXIT | F6 |

LESSON 5.7

LESSON 5.7 Graphing Calculator Keystrokes
For use with pages 382 and 383

TI-83 Plus

Example 5

Y= X,T,θ,n ^ 6 − 2 X,T,θ,n ^ 5
+ 3 X,T,θ,n ^ 4 − 1 0 X,T,θ,n MATH
3 − 6 X,T,θ,n x^2 − 8 X,T,θ,n − 8
ENTER
WINDOW (−) 5 ENTER 5 ENTER 1 ENTER
(−) 1 0 0 ENTER 4 0 ENTER 2 0 ENTER
GRAPH 2nd [CALC] 2

Press ◄ until the cursor is to the left of a zero. ENTER

Press ► until the cursor is to the right of a zero. ENTER

Press ◄ until the cursor appears to be on the zero. ENTER

Example 6

Y= 0 · 0 0 5 4 7 X,T,θ,n MATH 3 − 0
· 2 2 5 X,T,θ,n x^2 + 3 · 6 2
X,T,θ,n − 2 6 · 0 ENTER
WINDOW (−)
1 0 ENTER 4 0 ENTER 1 0 ENTER (−) 4 0
ENTER 4 0 ENTER 1 0 ENTER
GRAPH 2nd
[CALC] 2

Press ◄ until the cursor is to the left of a zero. ENTER

Press ► until the cursor is to the right of a zero. ENTER

Press ◄ until the cursor appears to be on the zero. ENTER

Casio CFX-9850GC Plus

Example 5

From the main menu, choose GRAPH.

X,θ,T ^ 6 − 2 X,θ,T ^ 5 + 3
X,θ,T ^ 4 − 1 0 X,θ,T ^ 3 − 6
X,θ,T x^2 − 8 X,θ,T − 8 EXE
SHIFT F3 (−) 5 EXE 5 EXE 1 EXE (−)
1 0 0 EXE 4 0 EXE 2 0 EXE EXIT
F6 SHIFT F5 F1

Example 6

From the main menu, choose GRAPH.

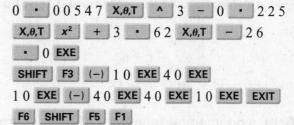

0 · 0 0 5 4 7 X,θ,T ^ 3 − 0 · 2 2 5
X,θ,T x^2 + 3 · 6 2 X,θ,T − 2 6
· 0 EXE
SHIFT F3 (−) 1 0 EXE 4 0 EXE
1 0 EXE (−) 4 0 EXE 4 0 EXE 1 0 EXE EXIT
F6 SHIFT F5 F1

LESSON 5.7 Practice A
For use with pages 379–386

Identify the number of solutions or zeros.

1. $2x^2 + 5x - 9 = 0$

2. $f(t) = t^3 + 4t^2 - 7$

3. $g(z) = -z^3 + z^2 + 6z - 3$

4. $x^4 - 6x^2 + 8x - 12 = 0$

5. $h(x) = 2x^5 - 3x^4 + x - 9$

6. $-6x^4 + 7x^2 - 15 = 0$

7. $f(y) = -2y + 3$

8. $3r^3 - r^2 + 5r - 21 = 0$

Given that $f(x)$ has real coefficients and $x = k$ is a zero, what other number must be a zero?

9. $k = 3 - \sqrt{2}$

10. $k = i$

11. $k = -2 - 9i$

12. $k = \sqrt{3} - i$

13. $k = 1 + \sqrt{5}\,i$

14. $k = \sqrt{2} + \sqrt{7}\,i$

Find all the zeros of the polynomial function.

15. $g(x) = x^3 - 8x^2 - 15x + 54$

16. $f(x) = x^4 - 3x^3 - 17x^2 + 39x - 20$

17. $h(x) = x^3 + 6x^2 + x + 6$

18. $g(x) = x^3 + 8x^2 - 7x - 56$

19. $f(x) = x^3 - 2x^2 + 9x - 18$

20. $h(x) = x^4 - x^2 - 20$

Write a polynomial function f of least degree that has rational coefficients, a leading coefficient of 1, and the given zeros.

21. -9

22. $-5, 4$

23. $-3, -1$

24. $-1, 0, 1$

25. $-1, 2, 6$

26. $-2, -1, 10$

27. The graph $f(x) = x^3 - x^2 - 8x + 12$ is shown at the right. How many real zeros does the function have? How many imaginary zeros does the function have?

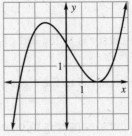

28. **Geometry** A square piece of sheet metal is 10 inches by 10 inches. Squares of side length x are cut from the corners and the remaining piece is folded to make an open box. The volume of the box is modeled by $V(x) = 4x^3 - 40x^2 + 100x$. What size square(s) can be cut from the corners to give a box with a volume of 25 cubic inches?

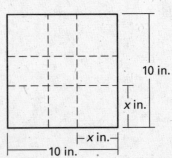

Practice B
For use with pages 379–386

Identify the number of solutions or zeros.

1. $f(x) = 5x^3 - 6x^2 + 2x - 3$

2. $g(s) = 8s^6 - 3s^4 - 11s^3 - 2s^2 + 4$

3. $-3y^7 + 5y^5 - 12y + 2 = 6$

4. $4 - 7x = x^2 - 3x^5$

Find all the zeros of the polynomial function.

5. $h(x) = x^3 - 3x^2 - x + 3$

6. $f(x) = x^4 - 4x^3 - 20x^2 + 48x$

7. $g(x) = x^3 + 5x^2 + x + 5$

8. $g(x) = x^4 - 9x^3 + 23x^2 - 81x + 126$

9. $f(x) = x^3 - x^2 - 11x + 3$

10. $h(x) = 2x^4 + x^3 + x^2 + x - 1$

Write a polynomial function f of least degree that has rational coefficients, a leading coefficient of 1, and the given zeros.

11. $-7, -4$

12. $1, 2, 5$

13. $-3, 0, 1$

14. $4, i, -i$

15. $-5, 0, -2i, 2i$

16. $8, 2 + i$

17. **Multiple Choice** Which is *not* a possible classification of the zeros of $f(x) = x^4 + 2x^3 - 7x^2 - 7x + 3$ according to Descartes' rule of signs?

   A. 2 positive real zeros, 2 negative real zeros, and 0 imaginary zeros

   B. 0 positive real zeros, 2 negative real zeros, and 2 imaginary zeros

   C. 0 positive real zeros, 0 negative real zeros, and 4 imaginary zeros

   D. 1 positive real zero, 1 negative real zero, and 2 imaginary zeros

Use a graphing calculator to graph the function. Then use the *zero* (or *root*) feature to approximate the real zeros of the function.

18. $g(x) = x^3 - x^2 - 5x + 3$

19. $h(x) = 2x^3 - x^2 - 3x - 1$

20. $f(x) = x^4 - 2x - 1$

21. $g(x) = x^4 - x^3 - 20x^2 + 10x + 27$

22. **Sporting Goods** For 1998 through 2005, the sales S (in billions of dollars) of sporting goods can be modeled by

$$S = 0.007t^3 + 0.1t^2 + 1.4x + 70$$

where t is the number of years since 1998. In which year were sales about $78 billion?

23. **Grocery Store Revenue** For the 25 years that a grocery store has been open, its annual revenue R (in millions of dollars) can be modeled by

$$R = \frac{1}{10,000}(-t^4 + 12t^3 - 77t^2 + 600t + 13,650)$$

where t is the number of years the store has been open. In what year(s) was the revenue $1.5 million?

LESSON 5.7 Practice C
For use with pages 379–386

Find all the zeros of the polynomial function.

1. $f(x) = x^4 + 4x^3 - 6x^2 - 36x - 27$

2. $h(x) = x^4 - 4x^3 + 4x - 1$

3. $g(x) = 2x^5 - 4x^4 - 2x^3 + 28x^2$

4. $g(x) = 2x^4 - x^3 - 42x^2 + 16x + 160$

5. $h(x) = 2x^4 - 7x^3 - 27x^2 + 63x + 81$

6. $f(x) = x^3 + 2x^2 + 4x - 7$

7. $g(x) = x^4 + 2x^3 + 2x - 1$
(*Hint:* $-i$ is a zero.)

8. $h(x) = x^4 - 2x^3 + 14x^2 + 6x - 5$
(*Hint:* $1 + 4i$ is a zero.)

Write a polynomial function f of least degree that has rational coefficients, a leading coefficient of 2, and the given zeros.

9. $-4, 0, 2, 4$

10. $2i, -2i, 5i, -5i$

11. $-5, \sqrt{3}$

12. $0, 3 + 4i$

13. $1, 2, 4 + \sqrt{2}$

14. $0, 3, i, 5 - 2i$

Determine the possible numbers of positive real zeros, negative real zeros, and imaginary zeros for the function.

15. $h(x) = x^3 - 4x^2 + 5x + 9$

16. $g(x) = x^4 + 3x^2 - 10x + 16$

17. $f(x) = x^5 - 6x^4 - 3x^3 + 7x^2 - 8x + 1$

18. $g(x) = x^{10} - x^8 + x^6 - x^4 + x^2 - 1$

19. $f(x) = x^6 + 2x^5 - 12x^4 - x^3 + 7x^2 + 5x - 16$

Use a graphing calculator to graph the function. Then use the *zero* (or *root*) feature to approximate the real zeros of the function.

20. $g(x) = x^4 + 3x^2 - 2$

21. $h(x) = x^5 + 12x^3 - 4x^2 + 16x + 25$

22. $f(x) = -x^6 + 4x^5 - 2x^2 + 9$

23. $g(x) = 3x^6 + 5x^5 - 30x^4 - 37x^3 - 25x^2$

24. Critical Thinking The graph of a polynomial of degree 5 has four distinct x-intercepts. What can be said about one of its zeros? Sketch a graph of this situation.

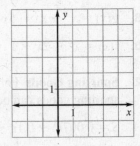

25. Critical Thinking Find a counterexample to disprove the following statement.

The polynomial function of least degree with integer coefficients and zeros at $x = -4, x = 2$, and $x = 5$, is unique.

26. College Tuition For 1998 through 2005, the enrollment E and cost of tuition T (in dollars) can be modeled by

$$E = -29.881t^2 + 190t + 4935 \text{ and } T = 10.543t^3 - 118.83t^2 + 921t + 9979$$

where t is the number of years since 1998.

a. Write a model that represents the total tuition R brought in by the college in a given year.

b. In which year did the college take in $62,638,000 in tuition?

LESSON 5.7 Study Guide
For use with pages 379–386

GOAL Classify the zeros of polynomial functions.

> **Vocabulary**
>
> When a factor of a polynomial appears more than once, you can count its solution more than once. The repeated factor produces a **repeated solution**.

EXAMPLE 1 Find the zeros of a polynomial function

Find all zeros of $f(x) = x^5 - x^4 - 7x^3 + 11x^2 + 16x - 20$.

Solution

STEP 1 Find the 5 rational zeros of f. The possible rational zeros are: $x = \pm1, \pm2, \pm4, \pm5, \pm10,$ and ±20. Using synthetic division you find that -2 is a zero repeated twice and 1 is also a zero.

STEP 2 Write $f(x)$ in factored form. Dividing f by its known factors $x + 2, x + 2,$ and $x - 1$ gives a quotient of $x^2 - 4x + 5$. So,
$$f(x) = (x - 1)(x + 2)^2(x^2 - 4x + 5).$$

STEP 3 Find the complex zeros of f. Use the quadratic formula to factor the trinomial into linear factors.
$$f(x) = (x - 1)(x + 2)^2[x - (2 + i)][x - (2 - i)]$$

The zeros are $-2, -2, 1, 2 + i,$ and $2 - i$.

EXAMPLE 2 Use zeros to write a polynomial function

Write a polynomial function that has rational coefficients, a leading coefficient of 1, and 4 and $1 + \sqrt{2}$ as zeros.

Solution

Because the coefficients are rational and $1 + \sqrt{2}$ is a zero, $1 - \sqrt{2}$ is a zero by the irrational conjugates theorem. Use the zeros and the factor theorem to write $f(x)$ as a product of three factors.

$f(x) = (x - 4)[x - (1 + \sqrt{2})][x - (1 - \sqrt{2})]$	Write $f(x)$ in factored form.
$= (x - 4)[(x - 1) - \sqrt{2}][(x - 1) + \sqrt{2}]$	Regroup terms.
$= (x - 4)[(x - 1)^2 - (\sqrt{2})^2]$	Multiply.
$= (x - 4)[(x^2 - 2x + 1) - 2]$	Expand binomial.
$= (x - 4)(x^2 - 2x - 1)$	Simplify.
$= x^3 - 2x^2 - x - 4x^2 + 8x + 4$	Multiply.
$= x^3 - 6x^2 + 7x + 4$	Combine like terms.

Study Guide *continued*
For use with pages 379–386

Exercises for Examples 1 and 2

Find all zeros of the function.

1. $f(x) = x^3 - 2x^2 + 3x - 2$

2. $f(x) = x^4 - 4x^3 + 5x^2 - 2x - 12$

Write a polynomial function f of least degree that has rational coefficients, a leading coefficient of 1, and the given zeros.

3. $-2, -1, 1$

4. $3, 1 + \sqrt{2}$

5. $i, 4$

6. $i, 2 - \sqrt{3}$

EXAMPLE 3
Use Descartes' rule of signs

Determine the possible numbers of positive real zeros, negative real zeros, and imaginary zeros for $f(x) = x^4 + 2x^3 - x^2 + 3x + 5$.

Solution

The coefficients of $f(x) = x^4 + 2x^3 - x^2 + 3x + 5$ have 2 sign changes, so f has 2 or 0 positive real zero(s).

$$f(-x) = (-x)^4 + 2(-x)^3 - (-x)^2 + 3(-x) + 5$$
$$= x^4 - 2x^3 - x^2 - 3x + 5$$

The coefficients in $f(-x)$ have 2 sign changes, so f has 2 or 0 negative real zero(s).

Positive real zeros	Negative real zeros	Imaginary zeros	Total zeros
2	2	0	4
2	0	2	4
0	2	2	4
0	0	4	4

Exercises for Example 3

Determine the possible numbers of positive real zeros, negative real zeros, and imaginary zeros for the function.

7. $g(x) = x^3 + x^2 - 3x - 7$

8. $h(x) = x^4 - 3x^3 + 4x - 2$

Name _____ Date _____

The items checked below were covered in class on (date missed) _____

Lesson 5.7: Apply the Fundamental Theorem of Algebra

_____ **Goal:** Classify the zeros of polynomial functions. (pp. 379–383)

Material Covered:

_____ Example 1: Find the number of solutions or zeros

_____ Guided Practice for Example 1

_____ Example 2: Find the zeros of a polynomial function

_____ Guided Practice for Example 2

_____ Review complex numbers

_____ Example 3: Use zeros to write a polynomial function

_____ Guided Practice for Example 3

_____ Example 4: Use Descartes' rule of signs

_____ Guided Practice for Example 4

_____ Example 5: Approximate real zeros

_____ Another way

_____ Example 6: Approximate real zeros of a polynomial model

_____ Guided Practice for Examples 5 and 6

Vocabulary:

repeated solution, p. 379

_____ Other (specify)

_____

_____

Homework and Additional Learning Support

_____ Textbook (specify) pp. 383–386

_____

_____ *Study Guide* worksheet (specify exercises)_____

_____ *@HomeTutor* for Lesson 5.7

LESSON 5.7

LESSON 5.7 Real-Life Application: When Will I Ever Use This?

For use with pages 379–386

High School Athletic Programs

You work for a sporting goods company that manufactures sports apparel for high school athletic programs. Your company is researching the recent trend of high school students who are participating in athletic programs.

Your company determines that the number of students S (in thousands) in the United States from 1990 to 2003 that participated in high school athletic programs can be modeled by the equation

$$S = 0.021t^5 - 0.572t^4 + 3.3t^3 + 16.173t^2 - 1.674t + 5267$$

where t represents the number of years since 1990.

1. Create a table of values for the model. According to your table, when did the number of students reach 5.8 million?

2. Sketch a graph of the model. Use a graphing calculator to verify your graph.

3. Write an equation that will determine the year the number of students reached 6 million. Then rewrite the equation by setting it equal to zero. Use a graphing calculator to approximate the real zero(s) of the rewritten equation.

4. Write an equation that will determine the year the number of students reached 6.6 million. Then rewrite the equation by setting it equal to zero. Use a graphing calculator to approximate the real zero(s) of the rewritten equation.

5. According to the model, during which year will the number of students that participate in high school athletic programs reach 9.4 million? 13.8 million?

6. In 2015, the goal of your company is to have at least 15% of the total number of students participating in high school athletic programs wearing its athletic apparel. Approximately how many high school students will be wearing the company's athletic apparel if the goal is reached?

Name _____   Date _____

In Exercises 1–4, determine whether the statement is *true* or *false*. Justify your reasoning.

1. A polynomial function can have no rational zeros but can have real zeros.

2. If a polynomial function has three real zeros, and only one of them is a rational number, then the other two zeros must be irrational numbers.

3. For a cubic polynomial function $f(x) = ax^3 + bx^2 + cx + d$ $(a \neq 0)$, it is possible that f has no real zeros.

4. For a fourth-degree polynomial function with rational coefficients, it is possible that the function has three rational zeros and one irrational zero.

In Exercises 5–8, write a polynomial function f of least degree that has rational coefficients, the given zeros, and the given function value.

5. Zeros: $2, 4i$; value: $f(1) = 17$

6. Zeros: $-1, 1 + 3i$; value: $f(0) = 5$

7. Zeros: $0, 6, -1 + \sqrt{5}$; value: $f(-3) = 9$

8. Zeros: $-4, 2 - \sqrt{3}$; value: $f(4) = 16$

9. **a.** Copy and complete the table.

Function	Zeros	Sum of zeros	Product of zeros
$f_1(x) = x^2 - x - 12$			
$f_2(x) = x^3 - 28x + 48$			
$f_3(x) = x^4 + 3x^3 + 11x^2 + 27x + 18$			
$f_4(x) = x^5 - 3x^4 - 6x^3 + 6x^2 + 8x$			

b. Use the table in part (a) to make a conjecture relating the sum of the zeros of a polynomial function with the coefficients of the polynomial function.

c. Use the table in part (a) to make a conjecture relating the product of the zeros of a polynomial function with the coefficients of the polynomial function.

10. **Biology** The concentration C of a chemical in a bloodstream t hours after injection into muscle tissue is given by

$$C = \frac{3t^2 + t}{t^3 + 50}, \quad t \geq 0.$$

Solve the related equation

$$3t^4 + 2t^3 - 300t - 50 = 0$$

to determine when the concentration is the greatest. Approximate this time to the nearest tenth of an hour.

LESSON 5.8

LESSON 5.8 Teaching Guide

Key Concept

You will use x-intercepts, a table of values, and the end behavior of a function to graph a polynomial function. You will determine the turning points of graphs by finding the local minimums and local maximums of the function.

Teaching the Lesson

Differentiating Instruction: See the Teacher's Edition side column notes on page 388 and the notes on differentiating instruction in the *Algebra 2 Toolkit*.

Teaching Notes and Suggested Questions: See the Teacher's Edition side columns on pages 387–389.

Activity Generator: See the Activity Generator Support Manual.

Animated Algebra: You may want to include the animation on page 388 in your lesson.

Starting the Lesson

Motivate the Lesson The interactive questions at the right guide students through a brief class activity that helps them explore the concepts of finding the turning points of graphs.

Alternative Lesson Starter

You may want to review prerequisite concepts, such as:

- graph quadratic functions (p. 245)

- end behavior of polynomial functions (p. 339)

- graph polynomial functions (p. 340)

Questions to Start the Lesson

1. A point on a graph of a polynomial function is a *turning point* if it is higher (or lower) than all of the nearby points on the graph. What are the turning points of the graph shown?

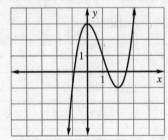

2. Use a graphing calculator to find the turning point(s) of the graph of $y = x^2 - 2x - 8$.

3. Use a graphing calculator to approximate the turning point(s) of the graph of $y = x^3 - 9x$.

Common Student Errors

- Erroneously believing that a polynomial function of degree n has *exactly* $(n - 1)$ turning points

  Tip Remind students that this is only true if a function also has n real zeros. Find turning points for functions with different degrees and less than $(n - 1)$ turning points.

The example below may be helpful.

$$f(x) = x^4 - x^3 + 2x^2 + 2x - 4$$

This function has degree 4 but only 1 turning point.

Teaching Strategy of the Day

Teacher Preparation During the last 5 minutes of class check for understanding using the Closing the Lesson feature in the Teacher's Edition or the Guided Practice Exercises in the Pupil's Edition.

Lesson Plan *continued*
Standard Schedule: 1 day lesson   Block Schedule: 0.5 day lesson with 5.7

GOAL Use intercepts to graph polynomial functions.

State Standards _____

Focus and Motivate	**Starting Options** _____ Homework Check (5.7): TE p. 384; Answer Transparencies _____ Daily Homework Quiz (5.7): TE p. 386 _____ Warm-Up: TE p. 387 or Transparencies _____ Starting the Lesson Questions: Teaching Guide _____ Motivating the Lesson: TE p. 388
Teach	**Teaching Options** _____ Essential Question: TE p. 387 _____ Alternative Lesson Openers: Electronic Classroom _____ Classroom Activity: Activity Generator; Chapter Resource Book p. 84–86 _____ Examples 1–3: PE pp. 387–389 _____ Extra Examples 1–3 with Key Questions: TE pp. 388–389 _____ Interdisciplinary Application: Chapter Resource Book p. 96 _____ Notetaking Guide pp. 154–156 **Checking for Understanding** _____ Closing the Lesson: TE p. 389 _____ Guided Practice Exercises: PE p. 389
Practice and Apply	**Assigning Homework** _____ Basic: Day 1: pp. 390–392 Exs. 1–8, 13–17, 21–26, 30, 39–42, 45–61 odd _____ Average: Day 1: pp. 390–392 Exs. 1, 2, 6–10, 13, 14, 18–21, 25–33, 39–43, 46, 49, 52, 53, 56, 60 _____ Advanced: Day 1: pp. 390–392 Exs. 1, 2, 11, 12, 21–44*, 47, 50, 54, 58, 62 _____ Block: pp. 390–392 Exs. 1, 2, 6–10, 13, 14, 18–21, 25–33, 39–43, 46, 49, 52, 53, 56, 60 (with 5.7) _____ Practice Masters: Chapter Resource Book pp. 87–92 (Levels A, B, or C)
Assess and Reteach	**Differentiating Instruction** _____ Study Guide: Chapter Resource Book pp. 93–94 _____ Tutorial Software _____ Challenge: Chapter Resource Book p. 97 _____ Remediation and Intervention Package: _____ _____ English Language Learners Package: _____ **Preparing for Standardized Tests** _____ Standardized Test Practice: PE pp. 390–392 Exs. 2, 21, 30, 32, 33, 43 **Assessing the Lesson** _____ Daily Homework Quiz (5.8): TE p. 392 or Transparencies

LESSON 5.8 Graphing Calculator Activity: Local Maximums and Minimums

For use before Lesson 5.8

QUESTION **How can you use a graphing calculator to find local maximums and minimums of a polynomial function?**

An important characteristic of graphs of polynomial functions is that they have *turning points* corresponding to the local maximum and minimum values.

You can use a graphing calculator to find these local maximums and minimums.

EXAMPLE **Find local maximums and minimums on a graphing calculator**

Use a graphing calculator to find the local maximums and minimums of the given function.

$y = x^3 - 7x + 6$

Solution

STEP 1 **Enter** the function.

STEP 2 **Graph** the function.

STEP 3 **Adjust** your viewing window so that you can see the local maximum and minimum.

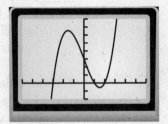

STEP 4 **Use** the *maximum* feature to find the local maximum. The local maximum is about $(-1.53, 13.13)$.

STEP 5 **Use** the *minimum* feature to find the local minimum. The local minimum is about $(1.53, -1.13)$.

PRACTICE **Use a graphing calculator to find the local maximums and minimums of the given function.**

1. $y = x^4 - 2x^3 - 10x^2 + 8x + 12$

2. $y = x^3 + 4x^2 + x - 6$

3. $y = x^4 - 13x^2 + 36$

4. $y = 2(x - 4)(x + 4)(x + 1)$

5. $y = -\frac{2}{3}(x - 1)(x + 2)(x + 1)(x - 3)$

6. $y = 0.4(x + 6)(x - 6)(x + 2)$

| LESSON 5.8 | # Graphing Calculator Activity: Local Maximums and Minimums *continued* |

For use before Lesson 5.8

TI-83 Plus

STEP 1

Y= | X,T,θ,n | MATH | 3 | − | 7 | X,T,θ,n | + | 6
ENTER

STEP 2

GRAPH

STEP 3

WINDOW | (−) | 1 0 | ENTER | 1 0 | ENTER | 1
ENTER | (−) | 1 0 | ENTER | 2 0 | ENTER | 1
ENTER | GRAPH

STEP 4

2nd | [CALC] 4

Press ◀ until the cursor is to the left of the local maximum. ENTER

Press ▶ until the cursor is to the right of the local maximum. ENTER

Press ◀ until the cursor appears to be on the local maximum. ENTER

STEP 5

2nd | [CALC] 3

Press ◀ until the cursor is to the left of the local minimum. ENTER

Press ▶ until the cursor is to the right of the local minimum. ENTER

Press ◀ until the cursor appears to be on the local minimum. ENTER

Casio CFX-9850GC Plus

STEP 1

From the main menu, choose GRAPH.

X,θ,T | ^ | 3 | − | 7 | X,θ,T | + | 6 | EXE

STEP 2

F6

STEP 3

SHIFT | F3 | (−) | 1 0 | EXE | 1 0 | EXE | 1 | EXE | (−)
1 0 | EXE | 2 0 | EXE | 1 | EXE | EXIT | F6

STEP 4

SHIFT | F5 | F3

STEP 5

SHIFT | F5 | F2

LESSON 5.8 Graphing Calculator Keystrokes
For use with page 388

TI-83 Plus

Example 2

a. `Y=` `X,T,θ,n` `MATH` 3 `–` 3 `X,T,θ,n`
   x^2 `+` 6 `ENTER` `ZOOM` 6

b. `Y=` `X,T,θ,n` `^` 4 `–` 6 `X,T,θ,n`
   `MATH` 3 `+` 3 `X,T,θ,n` `x²` `+` 1 0
   `X,T,θ,n` `–` 3 `ENTER` `ZOOM` 6

a. and b.

To find *x*-intercept:
`2nd` [CALC] 2

Press ◄ until the cursor is to the left of the zero. `ENTER`

Press ► until the cursor is to the right of the zero. `ENTER`

Press ◄ until the cursor appears to be on the zero. `ENTER`

To find local maximum:
`2nd` [CALC] 4

Press ◄ until the cursor is to the left of the local maximum. `ENTER`

Press ► until the cursor is to the right of the local maximum. `ENTER`

Press ◄ until the cursor appears to be on the local maximum. `ENTER`

To find local minimum:
`2nd` [CALC] 3

Press ◄ until the cursor is to the left of the local minimum. `ENTER`

Press ► until the cursor is to the right of the local minimum. `ENTER`

Press ◄ until the cursor appears to be on the local minimum. `ENTER`

Casio CFX-9850GC Plus

Example 2

a. From the main menu, choose GRAPH.
   `X,θ,T` `^` 3 `–` 3 `X,θ,T` `x²` `+` 6
   `EXE` `SHIFT` `F3` `F3` `EXIT` `F6`

b. From the main menu, choose GRAPH.
   `X,θ,T` `^` 4 `–` 6 `X,θ,T` `^` 3 `+` 3
   `X,θ,T` `x²` `+` 1 0 `X,θ,T` `–` 3 `EXE`
   `SHIFT` `F3` `F3` `EXIT` `F6`

a. and b.

To find *x*-intercept:
`SHIFT` `F5` `F1`

To find local maximum:
`SHIFT` `F5` `F2`

To find local minimum:
`SHIFT` `F5` `F3`

Name _____ Date _____

1. True or False If k is a zero of the polynomial function f, then k is an x-intercept of the graph of $f(x)$. *Explain* your answer.

Determine the lowest-degree polynomial that has the given graph.

2. 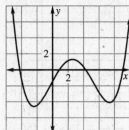   **3.** 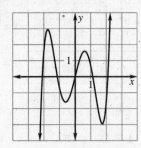   **4.**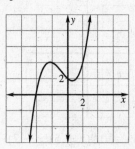

Estimate the coordinates of each turning point and state whether each corresponds to a local maximum or a local minimum.

5. 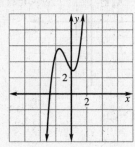   **6.** 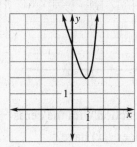   **7.**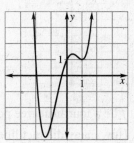

Match the graph with its function.

8. $f(x) = 2x^4 - 3x^2 - 2$ **9.** $f(x) = 2x^6 - 6x^4 + 4x^2 - 2$ **10.** $f(x) = -2x^4 + 3x^2 - 2$

A. 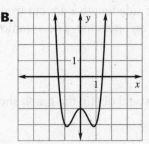   **B.**   **C.**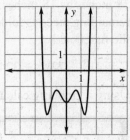

Determine the x-intercepts of the function.

11. $g(x) = (x + 4)(x - 1)$ **12.** $h(x) = (x - 2)(x - 3)$

13. $f(x) = x(x + 4)(x - 5)$ **14.** $f(x) = (x + 3)(x + 1)(x - 8)$

15. $g(x) = (x + 6)^2$ **16.** $h(x) = (x - 1)(x - 7)^2$

LESSON
5.8

Practice A *continued*
For use with pages 387–392

Graph the function.

17. $f(x) = (x + 1)(x - 2)$

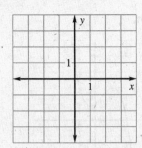

18. $g(x) = (x - 3)(x - 1)$

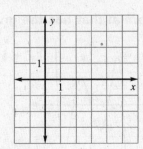

19. $h(x) = (x + 6)(x + 7)$

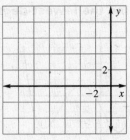

20. $h(x) = 0.9(x + 5)(x - 2)$

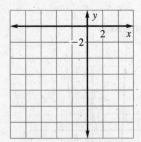

21. $g(x) = (x - 3)^2$

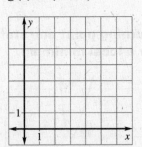

22. $f(x) = (x + 1)(x - 1)(x - 3)$

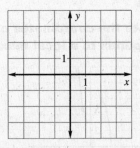

23. Let f be a fourth-degree polynomial function with the zeros -2, 6, $2i$, and $-2i$.

   a. How many distinct linear factors does $f(x)$ have?

   b. How many distinct solutions does $f(x) = 0$ have?

   c. What are the x-intercepts of the graph of f?

24. **Manufacturing** You are designing an open box from a piece of cardboard that is 18 inches by 18 inches. Squares of side length x are cut from the corners and the remaining piece is folded to make an open box. The volume of the box is given by the function

$$V = 4x^3 - 72x^2 + 324x.$$

Using a graphing calculator, you would obtain the graph shown below.

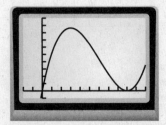

   a. What is the domain of the volume function? *Explain.*

   b. Use the graph to estimate the length of the cut x that will maximize the volume of the box.

   c. Estimate the maximum volume the box can have.

LESSON 5.8 Practice B
For use with pages 387–392

1. Describe and correct the error in the following statement.

   If −6 is a solution of the polynomial equation $f(x) = 0$, then −6 is a factor of $f(x)$.

State the maximum number of turns in the graph of the function.

2. $f(x) = x^4 + 2x^2 + 4$
3. $f(x) = -3x^3 + x^2 - x + 5$
4. $g(x) = 2x^6 + 1$

5. $g(x) = 4x^2 - 5x + 3$
6. $h(x) = 3x^7 - 6x^2 + 7$
7. $h(x) = 2x^9 - 8x^7 + 7x^5$

Determine the *x*-intercepts of the function.

8. $g(x) = (x + 3)(x - 2)(x - 5)$
9. $h(x) = (x + 4)(x - 6)(x - 8)$

10. $f(x) = (x + 3)^2(x - 2)$
11. $f(x) = (x + 5)(x + 1)(x - 7)$

12. $g(x) = (x + 6)^3(x + 2)$
13. $h(x) = (x - 8)^5$

Graph the function.

14. $f(x) = (x - 3)(x + 2)(x + 1)$
15. $g(x) = (x - 3)^2(x + 2)$

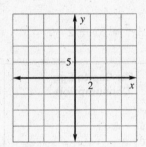
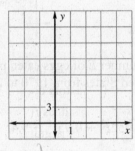

16. $h(x) = 0.3(x + 6)(x - 1)(x - 4)$
17. $g(x) = \frac{5}{6}(x + 1)^2(x - 1)(x - 4)$

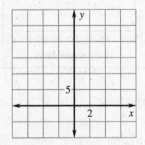
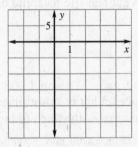

18. $h(x) = (x - 1)(x^2 + x + 1)$
19. $f(x) = (x + 2)(x^2 + 2x + 2)$

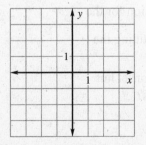
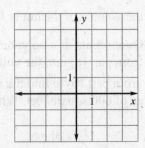

LESSON 5.8 Practice B *continued*
For use with pages 387–392

Estimate the coordinates of each turning point and state whether each corresponds to a local maximum or a local minimum. Then estimate all real zeros and determine the least degree the function can have.

20.

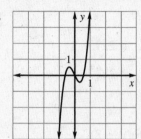

21.

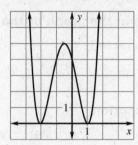

22.

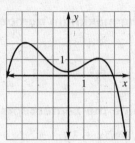

Use a graphing calculator to graph the function. Identify the x-intercepts and points where local maximums or local minimums occur.

23. $f(x) = 3x^3 - 9x + 1$

24. $h(x) = -\frac{1}{3}x^3 + x - \frac{2}{3}$

25. $g(x) = -\frac{1}{4}x^4 + 2x^2$

26. $f(x) = x^5 - 6x^3 + 9x$

27. $h(x) = x^5 - 5x^3 + 4x$

28. $g(x) = x^4 - 2x^3 - 3x^2 + 5x + 2$

29. Food The average number E of eggs eaten per person each year in the United States from 1970 to 2000 can be modeled by

$$E = 0.000944t^4 - 0.052t^3 + 0.95t^2 - 9.4t + 308$$

where t is the number of years since 1970. Graph the function and identify any turning points on the interval $0 \le t \le 30$. What real-life meaning do these points have?

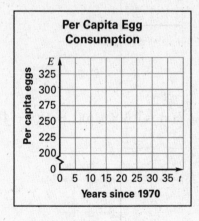

30. Quonset Huts A Quonset hut is a dwelling shaped like half a cylinder. You have 600 square feet of material with which to build a Quonset hut.

a. The formula for surface area is $S = \pi r^2 + \pi r\ell$ where r is the radius of the semicircle and ℓ is the length of the hut. Substitute 600 for S and solve for ℓ.

b. The formula for the volume of the hut is $V = \frac{1}{2}\pi r^2\ell$. Write an equation for the

volume V of the Quonset hut as a polynomial function of r by substituting the expression for ℓ from part (a) into the volume formula.

c. Use the function from part (b) to find the maximum volume of a Quonset hut with a surface area of 600 square feet. What are the hut's dimensions?

Practice C
For use with pages 387–392

State the minimum number of turns in the graph of the function.

1. $f(x) = x^4 + 3x^3 - 2x + 5$ **2.** $f(x) = 4 - 2x^2 + 5x^3$ **3.** $g(x) = 2x - 3x^5 + 2x^2 - 5$

Graph the function and state the domain and range.

4. $f(x) = (x + 1)(x^2 + 1)$

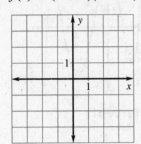

5. $g(x) = x(x + 2)^2(x - 1)^2$

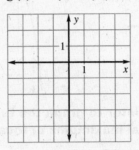

6. $h(x) = (x - 1)(x + 1)^3(x - 2)^2$

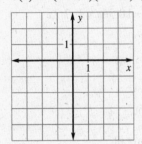

7. $h(x) = -x^2(x - 3)(x - 2)^3$

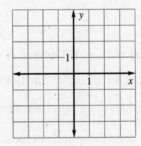

8. $g(x) = x(x + 1)(x - 1)^2(x - 3)^3$

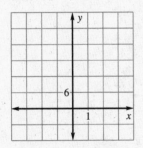

9. $f(x) = x^3(x + 3)^2(x^2 + x + 2)$

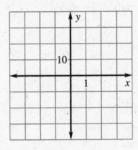

10. $f(x) = x^2(x + 1)(x - 1)^2(x - 3)^3$

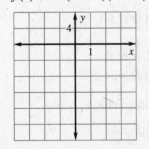

11. $g(x) = (x + 7)^2(x + 4)^2(x + 2)^3$

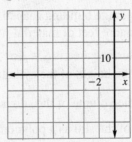

LESSON 5.8

Practice C *continued*
For use with pages 387–392

Estimate the coordinates of each turning point and state whether each corresponds to a local maximum or a local minimum. Then estimate all real zeros and determine the least degree the function can have.

12.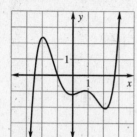

13.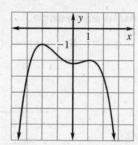

14.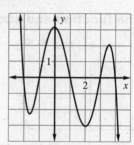

Use a graphing calculator to graph the function. Identify the x-intercepts and points where local maximums or local minimums occur.

15. $f(x) = x^5 - 2x^4 - x^3 + 3x + 1$

16. $g(x) = 3x^3 - 6x + x^4$

17. $h(x) = -\frac{1}{5}x^5 - \frac{7}{8} + x^2$

18. $f(x) = x^4 + 2.6x^3 - 10.56x^2 + 7.2x$

Consider the graphs $f(x) = (x + 1)^n$ where $n = 1, 2, 3, 4,$ and 5.

19. What is the x-intercept for all of the functions?

20. For what values of n does the graph have a turning point at the x-intercept?

21. For what values of n does the graph not have a turning point at the x-intercept?

22. Generalize your findings in Exercises 20 and 21. Test your theory by graphing $f(x) = (x + 1)^6$ and $g(x) = (x + 1)^7$.

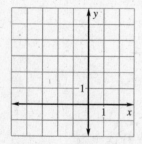

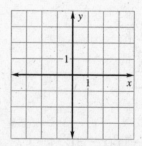

23. **Storage** A silo is a storage building shaped like a cylinder with half a sphere on top. A farmer has 1000 square feet of material with which to build a silo.

   a. The formula for surface area is $S = 4\pi r^2 + 2\pi rh$ where r is the radius of the cylinder and h is the height of the cylinder. Substitute 1000 for S and solve for h.

   b. The formula for the volume of the silo is $V = \frac{2}{3}\pi r^3 + \pi r^2 h$. Write an equation for the volume V of the silo as a polynomial function of r by substituting the expression for h from part (a) into the volume formula.

   c. Use the function from part (b) to find the maximum volume of a silo with a surface area of 1000 square feet. What are the silo's dimensions?

Study Guide
For use with pages 387–392

GOAL Use intercepts to graph polynomial functions.

> ## Vocabulary
>
> The y-coordinate of a turning point is a **local maximum** of the function if the point is higher than all nearby points.
>
> The y-coordinate of a turning point is a **local minimum** of the function if the point is lower than all nearby points.

EXAMPLE 1 ## Use x-intercepts to graph a polynomial function

Graph the function $f(x) = \frac{1}{5}(x - 3)^2(x + 1)^2$.

STEP 1 Use the x-intercepts. Because -1 and 3 are zeros of f, plot $(-1, 0)$ and $(3, 0)$.

STEP 2 Plot points between and beyond the x-intercepts.

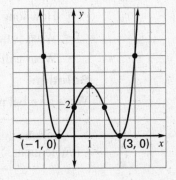

x	-2	-1	0	1	2	3	4
y	5	0	$\frac{9}{5}$	$\frac{16}{5}$	$\frac{9}{5}$	0	5

STEP 3 Determine end behavior. Because f has four factors of the form $x - k$ and a constant factor of $\frac{1}{5}$, it is a quartic function with a positive leading coefficient. So, $f(x) \to \infty$ as $x \to -\infty$ and $f(x) \to \infty$ as $x \to \infty$.

STEP 4 Draw the graph so that it passes through the plotted points and has the appropriate end behavior.

EXAMPLE 2 ## Find turning points

Graph the function $h(x) = -x^4 - 2x^3 + 3x^2 + 4x - 4$. Identify the x-intercepts and the points where the local maximums and local minimums occur.

Use a graphing calculator to graph the function. The graph of h has two x-intercepts and three turning points. Use the calculator's *zero*, *minimum*, and *maximum* features to approximate the coordinates of the points.

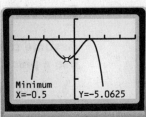

The x-intercepts are $x = -2$ and $x = 1$. The function has a local minimum at $(-0.5, -5.0625)$. The function has local maximums at $(-2, 0)$ and $(1, 0)$.

**LESSON
5.8**
Study Guide   *continued*
For use with pages 387–392

Exercises for Examples 1 and 2

Graph the function. Identify the *x*-intercepts and the points where the local maximums and local minimums occur.

1. $f(x) = \frac{1}{2}x^3 - 6x - 8$ **2.** $f(x) = x^3 + 5x^2 + 7x + 3$

EXAMPLE 3 ## Maximize a polynomial model

Metal Box You are making an open rectangular box out of a piece of metal. The box will be formed by making the cuts shown in the diagram and folding up the sides so that the flaps are square. The cardboard has a width of 4 inches and a length of 12 inches. You want the box to have the greatest volume possible.

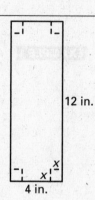

12 in.

4 in.

- How long should you make the cuts?
- What is the maximum volume?
- What will be the dimensions of the finished box?

Solution

Write a verbal model for the volume. Then write a function.

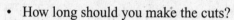

Volume (cubic inches)	=	Length (inches)	·	Width (inches)	·	Height (inches)

$V \quad = (12 - 2x) \quad · \quad (4 - 2x) \quad · \quad x$

$\quad = (48 - 32x + 4x^2)\,x \qquad$ Use FOIL method.

$\quad = 4x^3 - 32x^2 + 48x \qquad$ Write in standard form.

To find the maximum volume, graph the volume function on a graphing calculator using $0 < x < 2$ from the physical restrictions on the size of the flaps. From the graph, you can see that the maximum volume is about 20.2 and occurs when $x \approx 0.9$.

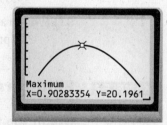

Maximum
X=0.90283354 Y=20.1961

The maximum volume is about 20.2 cubic inches. The dimensions of the box are about 10.2 inches, by 2.2 inches by 0.9 inch.

Exercises for Example 3

Assume that a box is constructed using the method in Example 3. You use a piece of cardboard that is 6 inches by 12 inches.

3. What are the dimensions of the box with the maximum volume?

4. What is the maximum volume?

Quick Catch-Up for Absent Students
For use with pages 387–392

The items checked below were covered in class on (date missed) _____

Lesson 5.8: Analyze Graphs of Polynomial Functions

_____ **Goal:** Use intercepts to graph polynomial functions. (pp. 387–389)

Material Covered:

_____ Example 1: Use *x*-intercepts to graph a polynomial function

_____ Example 2: Find turning points

_____ Find maximums and minimums

_____ Example 3: Maximize a polynomial model

_____ Guided Practice for Examples 1, 2, and 3

Vocabulary:

      local maximum, p. 388   local minimum, p. 388

_____ Other (specify)

_____

Homework and Additional Learning Support

_____ Textbook (specify) pp. 390–392

_____

_____ *Study Guide* worksheet (specify exercises)_____

_____ *@HomeTutor* for Lesson 5.8

LESSON 5.8 Interdisciplinary Application
For use with pages 387–392

Measuring Precipitation

Science A rain gauge is the most common instrument used to measure the amount of rain that falls in a certain place over a specified length of time. The gauge consists of a cylinder with a narrow tube inside and a funnel on top. Rain falls into the funnel and down into the tube where it is measured. The mouth of the funnel has an area ten times that of the tube. So, an inch of rain that falls into the funnel would fill ten inches of the tube. A special ruler is used to measure the amount of rain in the tube.

Today's technology allows meteorologists to measure rainfall using radar. This electronic instrument sends out radio waves that are reflected by raindrops. These reflected waves indicate the amount and intensity of rainfall.

If an amount of rainfall is too small to be measured, it is called a *trace of rain*. Rainfall from a trace to 0.10 inch per hour is considered *light rain*, 0.11 to 0.30 inch per hour is a *moderate rain*, and anything greater than 0.30 inch per hour is classified as a *heavy rain*.

Average annual rainfall amounts vary throughout the world. Some factors that affect rainfall are latitude, bodies of water, mountains, air currents, and cities. Near the equator, the heat of the sun causes large amounts of moisture to evaporate into the air, while near the poles, it is so cold that the air cannot hold much moisture. The greatest amount of rainfall in the world occurs at Lloro, Colombia where an average of 523.6 inches of rain falls each year. The least amount of rainfall occurs at Arica, Chile, which receives an average of 0.03 inch each year.

In Exercises 1–3, use the following information.

The normal monthly precipitation P (in inches) in Honolulu, Hawaii for each month of the year can be approximated by the model

$$P = -0.0021t^4 + 0.0564t^3 - 0.4217t^2 + 0.6101t + 2.46$$

where $t = 1$ represents January.

1. Sketch a graph of the model for $1 \leq t \leq 12$.

2. From your graph, determine the month that has the greatest amount of precipitation and the least amount of precipitation.

3. What is the normal annual precipitation in Honolulu, Hawaii? Round your result to two decimal places.

Challenge Practice

For use with pages 387–392

In Exercises 1–4, solve the system of equations by graphing. Then verify the solution(s) algebraically.

1. $y = -2x^2 + 2$
$y = 2(x^4 - 2x^2 + 1)$

2. $y = x^3 - 3x^2 + 1$
$y = x^2 - 3x + 1$

3. $y = x^3 - 2x^2 + x - 1$
$y = -x^2 + 3x - 1$

4. $y = x^4 - 2x^2 + 1$
$y = -x^4 + 2x^2 - 1$

In Exercises 5–8, you can use the given related quadratic equation to determine where the local maximums and local minimums occur for the given cubic function. Solve the related quadratic equation. The solutions are the x-coordinates of the maximums or minimums. To determine the y-coordinates, evaluate the cubic function at the solutions of the quadratic equation.

Cubic Function	*Related Quadratic Equation*
5. $f(x) = x^3 + 7x^2 - 5x + 1$	$3x^2 + 14x - 5 = 0$
6. $f(x) = 2x^3 - 3x^2 - 36x + 24$	$6x^2 - 6x - 36 = 0$
7. $f(x) = -x^3 + 2x^2 + 4x + 6$	$-3x^2 + 4x + 4 = 0$
8. $f(x) = -2x^3 + 15x^2 + 36x - 1$	$-6x^2 + 30x + 36 = 0$

9. Consider the cubic functions and related quadratic equations given in Exercises 5–8. How is the coefficient of the x^3-term in the cubic function related to the coefficient of the x^2-term in the quadratic equation? How is the coefficient of the x^2-term in the cubic function related to the coefficient of the x-term in the quadratic equation? How is the coefficient of the x-term in the cubic function related to the constant term of the quadratic equation? Find a related quadratic equation for each cubic function below. Then determine where the local maximums and local minimums occur for each cubic function by solving the quadratic equation.

a. $f(x) = x^3 + 9x^2 + 24x + 3$
b. $f(x) = x^3 - x^2 - 8x + 8$
c. $f(x) = -2x^3 - 33x^2 - 60x + 12$

LESSON 5.9 Teaching Guide

Key Concept

You will use the graph of a function or finite differences to write the equation of a polynomial function. You will use the *regression* feature of a graphing calculator to find the *n*th degree polynomial function that best models a data set.

Teaching the Lesson

Differentiating Instruction: See the Teacher's Edition side column notes on page 394 and the notes on differentiating instruction in the *Algebra 2 Toolkit*.

Teaching Notes and Suggested Questions: See the Teacher's Edition side columns on pages 393–396.

Activity Generator: See the Activity Generator Support Manual.

Animated Algebra: You may want to include the animation on page 396 in your lesson.

Starting the Lesson

Motivate the Lesson The interactive questions at the right guide students through a brief class activity that helps them intuitively see and predict what information is needed to model polynomial functions.

Alternative Lesson Starter

You may want to review prerequisite concepts, such as:

*   writing a quadratic function given the function's graph (p. 309)

Questions to Start the Lesson

The table below shows the number *c* of coats sold at a department store for various months *m* during one year where $m = 1$ represents January.

m	1	3	5	7	9	11
c	100	80	30	5	40	160

1. Make a scatter plot of the data.

2. Suppose you want to model the data using a polynomial function. Do you think it would be best to use a linear function, a quadratic function, or a cubic function? Why?

3. Sketch the polynomial function you think best fits the data.

Common Student Errors

*   Confusion in determining an appropriate model that best fits a given data set

Tip Have students model a given set of data using each form of regression: *linear*, *quadratic*, *cubic*, and even *quartic regression*. Then students can graph each of the models to compare them to the original data.

Teaching Strategy of the Day

Testing Give students the opportunity to rework problems missed on a test. Have them return the test the next day with the missed problems corrected on a separate piece of paper.

LESSON 5.9	**Lesson Plan** continued

Standard Schedule: 2 day lesson   Block Schedule: 1 day lesson

GOAL   **Write higher-degree polynomial functions.**

State Standards _____

Focus and Motivate

Starting Options

_____ Homework Check (5.8): TE p. 390; Answer Transparencies
_____ Daily Homework Quiz (5.8): TE p. 392
_____ Warm-Up: TE p. 393 or Transparencies
_____ Starting the Lesson Questions: Teaching Guide
_____ Motivating the Lesson: TE p. 394

Teach

Teaching Options

_____ Essential Question: TE p. 393
_____ Alternative Lesson Openers: Electronic Classroom
_____ Classroom Activity: Activity Generator; Chapter Resource Book pp. 100–101
_____ Examples 1–4: PE pp. 393–396
_____ Extra Examples 1–4 with Key Questions: TE pp. 394–396
_____ Problem Solving Workshop: Mixed Problem Solving: Chapter Resource Book p. 108
_____ Notetaking Guide pp. 157–159

Checking for Understanding

_____ Closing the Lesson: TE p. 396
_____ Guided Practice Exercises: PE pp. 394–396

Practice and Apply

Assigning Homework

_____ Basic: Day 1: EP p. 1012 Exs. 35–38; pp. 397–399 Exs. 1–17; Day 2: pp. 397–399 Exs. 18, 19, 25–28, 31–44
_____ Average: Day 1: pp. 397–399 Exs. 1–5, 7–17, 22; Day 2: pp. 397–399 Exs. 18–21, 25–29, 31–44
_____ Advanced: Day 1: pp. 397–399 Exs. 1, 2, 4, 5, 7–17, 22, 23; Day 2: pp. 397–399 Exs. 18–21, 24–32*, 33–43 odd
_____ Block: pp. 397–399 Exs. 1–5, 7–22, 25–29, 31–44
_____ Practice Masters: Chapter Resource Book pp. 102–104 (Levels A, B, or C)

Assess and Reteach

Differentiating Instruction

_____ Study Guide: Chapter Resource Book pp. 105–106
_____ Tutorial Software
_____ Challenge: Chapter Resource Book p. 109
_____ Remediation and Intervention Package: _____
_____ English Language Learners Package: _____

Preparing for Standardized Tests

_____ Standardized Test Practice: PE pp. 397–398 Exs. 2, 10, 22, 23, 28
_____ Building Test-Taking Skills: PE pp. 408–411

Assessing the Lesson

_____ Daily Homework Quiz (5.9): TE p. 399 or Transparencies

LESSON 5.9 Graphing Calculator Keystrokes
For use with page 395

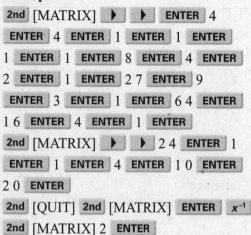

TI-83 Plus

Example 3

2nd [MATRIX] ▶ ▶ ENTER 4
ENTER 4 ENTER 1 ENTER 1 ENTER
1 ENTER 1 ENTER 8 ENTER 4 ENTER
2 ENTER 1 ENTER 2 7 ENTER 9
ENTER 3 ENTER 1 ENTER 6 4 ENTER
1 6 ENTER 4 ENTER 1 ENTER
2nd [MATRIX] ▶ ▶ 2 4 ENTER 1
ENTER 1 ENTER 4 ENTER 1 0 ENTER
2 0 ENTER
2nd [QUIT] 2nd [MATRIX] ENTER x⁻¹
2nd [MATRIX] 2 ENTER

Casio CFX-9850GC Plus

Example 3

From the main menu, choose MAT.

▶ 4 EXE 4 EXE 1 EXE 1 EXE 1 EXE 1
EXE 8 EXE 4 EXE 2 EXE 1 EXE 2 7
EXE 9 EXE 3 EXE 1 EXE 6 4 EXE 1 6
EXE 4 EXE 1 EXE
EXIT ▼ ▶ 4 EXE 1 EXE 1 EXE 4
EXE 1 0 EXE 2 0 EXE

From the main menu, choose RUN.

OPTN F2 F1 ALPHA [A] SHIFT [x⁻¹] F1
ALPHA [B] EXE

LESSON 5.9 Graphing Calculator Keystrokes
For use with page 396

TI-83 Plus

Example 4

STEP 1

| STAT | | ENTER | | 1 0 | ENTER | | 2 0 | | ENTER |

3 0 | ENTER | | 4 0 | ENTER | | 5 0 | ENTER | | 6 0

| ENTER | | 7 0 | ENTER | | 8 0 | ENTER | | 2 0 2 | · | 4

| ENTER | | 4 6 3 | · | 3 | ENTER | | 7 4 8 | · | 2

| ENTER | | 9 7 9 | · | 3 | ENTER | | 1 1 8 6 | · | 3

| ENTER | | 1 4 2 1 | · | 3 | ENTER | | 1 7 9 5 | · | 4

| ENTER | | 2 2 8 3 | · | 5 | ENTER | | 2nd |

[STAT PLOT] | ENTER | | ENTER | | ▼ |

| ENTER | | ▼ | | 2nd | [L1] | ENTER | | 2nd | [L2]

| ENTER | | ZOOM | | 9

STEP 2

| STAT | | ▶ | | 6 | 2nd | [L1] | , | 2nd | [L2] | , |

| VARS | | ▶ | | ENTER | | ENTER | | ENTER |

STEP 3

| GRAPH |

STEP 4

| Y= | | ▼ | | 4 4 0 0 | ENTER | | WINDOW |

| ENTER | | 1 2 0 | ENTER | | ENTER | | ENTER |

5 0 0 0 | ENTER | | GRAPH | | 2nd | [CALC] 5

| ENTER | | ENTER | | ENTER |

Casio CFX-9850GC Plus

Example 4

STEP 1

From the main menu, choose STAT.

1 0 | EXE | 2 0 | EXE | 3 0 | EXE | 4 0 | EXE | 5 0

| EXE | 6 0 | EXE | 7 0 | EXE | 8 0 | EXE | | ▶ | 2 0 2

· | 4 | EXE | 4 6 3 | · | 3 | EXE | 7 4 8 | · | 2 | EXE |

9 7 9 | · | 3 | EXE | 1 1 8 6 | · | 3 | EXE | 1 4 2 1

· | 3 | EXE | 1 7 9 5 | · | 4 | EXE | 2 2 8 3 | · | 5

| EXE | | F1 | | F6 | | ▼ | | F1 | | ▼ | | F1 | | ▼ | | F2 | | EXE |

| SHIFT | | F3 | 3 | EXE | 1 2 0 | EXE | 1 | EXE | | (−) | 1 5 2

| EXE | 5 0 0 0 | EXE | 1 | EXE | | EXIT | | F1 | | F1 |

STEP 2

| F2 | | F3 | | F4 |

STEP 3

| EXIT | | EXIT | | F1 | | F1 | | F4 | | F6 |

STEP 4

From the main menu, choose GRAPH.

0 | · | 0 0 6 5 0 1 2 | X,θ,T | | ^ | 3 | − |

0 | · | 7 3 9 3 6 6 8 | X,θ,T | | x² | | + |

4 8 | · | 9 5 6 2 0 4 9 | X,θ,T | | − |

2 3 5 | · | 8 8 5 7 1 | EXE | 4 4 0 0 | EXE | | SHIFT |

| F3 | 3 | EXE | 1 2 0 | EXE | 1 | (−) | 1 5 2 | EXE |

5 0 0 0 | EXE | | EXIT | | F6 | | SHIFT | | F5 | | F5 |

Name _____ Date _____

Practice A
For use with pages 393–399

Write the cubic function whose graph is shown.

1. 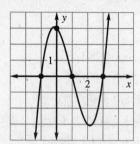 **2.** 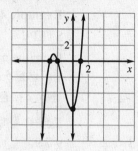 **3.**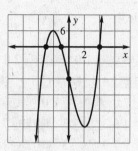

Write a cubic function whose graph passes through the points.

4. $(-4, 0), (-2, 0), (5, 0), (0, -40)$

5. $(-1, 0), (2, 0), (4, 0), (0, 8)$

6. $(1, 0), (2, 0), (3, 0), (0, -6)$

7. $(-3, 0), (-4, 0), (-5, 0), (0, 60)$

Show that the *n*th-order differences for the given function of degree *n* are nonzero and constant.

8. $f(x) = x^2 + 4x - 6$

9. $f(x) = x^3 - x^2 - 2x + 7$

Use finite differences to determine the degree of the polynomial function that will fit the data.

10.

x	1	2	3	4	5	6
f(x)	−1	3	3	5	15	39

11.

x	1	2	3	4	5	6
f(x)	0	8	12	12	8	0

12. **Hexagonal Numbers** A formula for the *n*th hexagonal number is $f(n) = n(2n - 1)$. Show that this function has constant second-order differences.

13. **Enrollment Rate** The table shows the percent enrollment rate *r* in preprimary schools from years 1970 to 2000.

Years since 1970, t	0	5	10	15	20	25	30
Enrollment rate, r	37.5	48.6	52.5	54.6	59.4	61.8	64

   a. Use a graphing calculator to find a polynomial model for the data.

   b. Predict the preprimary school enrollment rate in 2005.

LESSON 5.9

Practice B

For use with pages 393–399

Write the cubic function whose graph is shown.

1.

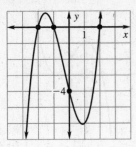

2.

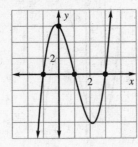

3.

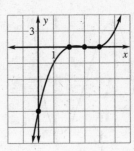

Write a cubic function whose graph passes through the points.

4. $(-2, 0), (0, 0), (1, 0), (2, 1)$

5. $(-4, 0), (-1, 0), (3, 0), (2, -2)$

6. $(-5, 0), (3, 0), (4, 0), (-1, -1)$

7. $(-3, 0), (0, 0), (1, 0), (-2, 4)$

Show that the *n*th-order differences for the given function of degree *n* are nonzero and constant.

8. $f(x) = -x^3 + 2x^2 - 1$

9. $f(x) = x^4 - 5x^3 + 3$

Use finite differences and a system of equations to find a polynomial function that fits the data.

10.

x	1	2	3	4	5	6
f(x)	5	19	49	101	181	295

11.

x	1	2	3	4	5	6
f(x)	-5	-6	-1	16	51	110

12. **Space Exploration** The table shows the average speed *y* (in feet per second) of a space shuttle for different times *t* (in seconds) after launch.

t	10	20	30	40	50	60	70	80
y	202.4	463.4	748.2	979.3	1186.3	1421.3	1795.4	2283.5

   a. Use a graphing calculator to find a polynomial model for the data.

   b. When the space shuttle reaches a speed of approximately 4400 feet per second, its booster rockets fall off. Use the model from part (a) to determine how long after launch this happens.

LESSON 5.9 **Practice C**
For use with pages 393–399

Write the cubic function whose graph is shown.

1. 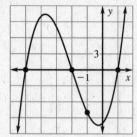 **2.** 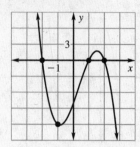 **3.**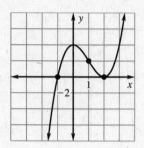

Write a cubic function whose graph passes through the points.

4. $(-1, 0), (2, 0), (3, 0), (0, 9)$

5. $\left(-\frac{1}{2}, 0\right), (1, 0), (3, 0), \left(0, \frac{9}{4}\right)$

6. $\left(\frac{1}{2}, 0\right), \left(\frac{3}{2}, 0\right), (3, 0), (0, 18)$

7. $\left(-\frac{1}{3}, 0\right), \left(\frac{1}{4}, 0\right), (1, 0), (2, 49)$

Show that the *n*th-order differences for the given function of degree *n* are nonzero and constant.

8. $f(x) = x^4 - 3x^3 - 2x$ **9.** $f(x) = 2x^3 - x + 4$

Use finite differences and a system of equations to find a polynomial function that fits the data.

10.

x	1	2	3	4	5	6
f(x)	10	29	76	157	278	445

11.

x	1	2	3	4	5	6
f(x)	−16	−31	−54	−79	−100	−111

12. Rent The table shows the median U.S. monthly rent r (in dollars) from years 1993 to 2003.

Years since 1993, t	0	2	4	6	7	8	10
Rent, r	487	523	549	580	602	633	651

a. Use a graphing calculator to find a polynomial model for the data.

b. Predict the median U.S. monthly rent in 2007.

c. Explain why you cannot use finite differences to find a model for the data.

LESSON 5.9 Study Guide
For use with pages 393–399

GOAL Write higher-degree polynomial functions.

> ### Vocabulary
> When the *x*-values in a data set are equally spaced, the differences of consecutive *y*-values are called **finite differences**.

EXAMPLE 1 Write a cubic function

Write the cubic function whose graph is shown.

STEP 1 Use the three given *x*-intercepts to write the function in intercept form.

$$f(x) = a(x + 3)(x + 1)(x - 1)$$

STEP 2 Find *a* by substituting the coordinates of the fourth point.

$$9 = a(-2 + 3)(-2 + 1)(-2 - 1)$$
$$a = 3$$

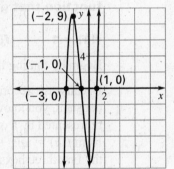

The function is $f(x) = 3(x + 3)(x + 1)(x - 1)$.

CHECK Check the end behavior for *f*. The degree of *f* is odd and $a > 0$. So, $f(x) \to +\infty$ as $x \to +\infty$ and $f(x) \to -\infty$ as $x \to -\infty$.

EXAMPLE 2 Find finite differences

The first four pentagonal numbers are shown below. A formula for the *n*th pentagonal number is $f(n) = \frac{1}{2}(3n^2 - n)$. Show that this function has constant second-order differences.

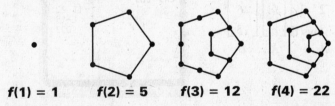

$f(1) = 1$ $f(2) = 5$ $f(3) = 12$ $f(4) = 22$

Write the first several pentagonal numbers. Find the first-order differences by subtracting consecutive pentagonal numbers. Then find the second-order differences by subtracting consecutive first-order differences.

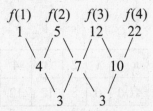

$f(1)$ $f(2)$ $f(3)$ $f(4)$ Write function values for equally-spaced *n*-values.
　1　　5　　12　　22

　　　4　　7　　10   First-order differences

　　　　3　　3   Second-order differences

Each second-order difference is 3, so the second-order differences are constant.

LESSON 5.9

Study Guide *continued*

For use with pages 393–399

Exercises for Examples 1 and 2

Write a cubic function whose graph passes through the given points.

1. $(-2, 0), (1, 0), (4, 0), (0, -8)$ 2. $(-5, 0), (-3, 0), (2, 0), (0, -30)$

3. Show that $f(n) = \frac{5}{2}n^2 + \frac{1}{2}n$ has constant second-order differences.

EXAMPLE 3 Model with finite differences

The first five hexagonal numbers are given below. Find a polynomial function that gives the nth hexagonal number.

$f(1) = 1$ $f(2) = 6$ $f(3) = 15$ $f(4) = 28$ $f(5) = 45$

Begin by finding the finite differences.

Because the second-order differences are constant, you know that the numbers can be represented by a quadratic function of the form $f(n) = an^2 + bn + c$. By substituting the first three hexagonal numbers into the function, you obtain a system of three linear equations in three variables.

$a(1)^2 + b(1) + c = 1 \rightarrow a + b + c = 1$

$a(2)^2 + b(2) + c = 6 \rightarrow 4a + 2b + c = 6$

$a(3)^2 + b(3) + c = 15 \rightarrow 9a + 3b + c = 15$

Write the linear system as a matrix equation $AX = B$. Enter the matrices A and B into a graphing calculator, and then calculate the solution $X = A^{-1}B$.

$$\begin{bmatrix} 1 & 1 & 1 \\ 4 & 2 & 1 \\ 9 & 3 & 1 \end{bmatrix} \begin{bmatrix} a \\ b \\ c \end{bmatrix} \begin{bmatrix} 1 \\ 6 \\ 15 \end{bmatrix}$$

$\quad\quad A \quad\quad X \quad B$

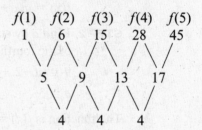

Calculate $X = A^{-1}B$.

The solution is $a = 2$, $b = -1$, and $c = 0$. So, the nth hexagonal number is given by $f(n) = 2n^2 - n$.

Exercise for Example 3

4. Use finite differences to find a polynomial function that fits the data in the table.

x	1	2	3	4	5	6
f(x)	0	8	12	12	8	0

LESSON 5.9 Quick Catch-Up for Absent Students
For use with pages 393–400

The items checked below were covered in class on (date missed) _____

Lesson 5.9: Write Polynomial Functions and Models

_____ **Goal:** Write higher-degree polynomial functions. (pp. 393–396)

Material Covered:

_____ Example 1: Write a cubic function

_____ Example 2: Find finite differences

_____ Guided Practice for Examples 1 and 2

_____ Example 3: Model with finite differences

_____ Review systems

_____ Guided Practice for Example 3

_____ Example 4: Solve a multi-step problem

_____ Another way

_____ Guided Practice for Example 4

Vocabulary:

finite differences, p. 393

_____ Other (specify)

_____

_____

Homework and Additional Learning Support

_____ Textbook (specify) pp. 397–399

_____

_____ *Study Guide* worksheet (specify exercises)_____

_____ @*HomeTutor* for Lesson 5.9

_____ Mixed Review of Problem Solving 5.6–5.9 (p. 400)

Problem Solving Workshop: Mixed Problem Solving

LESSONS 5.6–5.9

For use with pages 370–399

LESSON 5.9

1. **Multi-Step Problem** The volume of the pyramid shown is 120 cubic inches.

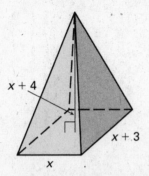

$x + 4$
$x + 3$
x

   a. Write a polynomial equation that you can use to find the value of x.

   b. Identify the possible rational solutions of the equation in part (a).

   c. Use synthetic division to find a rational solution of the equation. Show that no other real solutions exist.

   d. What are the dimensions of the pyramid?

2. **Multi-Step Problem** You want to make an open box from a piece of cardboard by cutting out the corners and folding up the sides. The original piece of cardboard is 17 inches by 11 inches.

   a. Write a polynomial function for the volume of the box.

   b. Graph the function in part (a).

   c. What are the dimensions of the box with the maximum volume?

   d. What is the maximum volume?

3. **Short Response** The table shows the average relationship between the years t since 1999 and the median cost c (in thousands of dollars) of a house in the United States. Use a graphing calculator to find a quadratic model for the data. Estimate the cost of a home in 2010.

t	0	1	2	3	4
c	161	169	175.2	187.6	195

4. **Gridded Answer** From 1980 to 2003, the total exports E (in billions of dollars) of the United States can be modeled by the function

   $$E = -0.165t^3 + 6.023t^2 - 30.728t + 247.432$$

   where t is the number of years since 1980. In which year was the total exports about $584.7 billion?

5. **Short Response** Your friend has started a dog walking service. The table shows the profit p (in dollars) of the service in the first 5 weeks. Use finite differences to find a polynomial model for the data. Then use the model to predict the profit in the eighth week.

Week, t	1	2	3	4	5
Profit, p	7	5	8	16	29

6. **Open-Ended** Write a polynomial function with rational coefficients that has 8 *possible* rational zeros according to the rational zero theorem, but no actual rational zeros.

7. **Extended Response** You are making a candle that is a right circular cone. You want the height of the cone to be 3 inches greater than the radius of the base. You want the candle to have a volume of 108π cubic inches.

   a. Let x represent the radius (in inches) of the base. Draw a diagram of the candle and label the dimensions in terms of x.

   b. Write a function that gives the volume V of the candle in terms of x.

   c. Graph the function in part (b). Use the graph to estimate the value of x for the candle.

   d. Write and solve an equation to find the value of x. *Compare* your answer with your estimate from part (c). What are the dimensions of the candle?

Name _____ Date _____

Challenge Practice

For use with pages 393–399

In Exercises 1 and 2, write a quartic function whose graph passes through the points.

1. $(-4, 0), (-1, 0), (1, 10), (2, 0), (3, 0)$

2. $(-5, 0), (-4, -21), (-3, 0), \left(-\frac{1}{2}, 0\right), (8, 0)$

In Exercises 3 and 4, write a quintic function whose graph passes through the points.

3. $(-3, 0), (-2, 0), (-1, 9), (0, 0), \left(\frac{1}{2}, 0\right), (2, 0)$

4. $(-5, 0), (-2, 0), (1, 0), (2, 14), (3, 0), (4, 0)$

5. **Temperatures** The table shows the monthly normal high temperatures H and monthly normal low temperatures L (in degrees Fahrenheit) for Silver City. In the table, t is the time in months, with $t = 1$ corresponding to January.

t	1	2	3	4	5	6	7	8	9	10	11	12
H	29	31	39	51	64	75	80	78	70	58	45	34

t	1	2	3	4	5	6	7	8	9	10	11	12
L	19	19	25	35	46	55	60	59	54	44	33	24

a. Find the fourth-order differences for the data in each table. Using your results, do you think each set of data can be modeled by a quartic function?

b. Use a graphing utility to find a quartic model for each set of data.

c. Use a graphing utility to graph each model from part (b) in the same viewing window.

d. Determine where the local maximum and local minimum occur for each model in part (b). What do these values represent in the context of the problem?

e. During what part of the year is the difference between the normal high and low temperatures greatest? When is it smallest?

f. The sun is northernmost in the sky around June 21. Does this agree with your answer for the local maximum in part (d)? If not, approximate the lag time of the temperatures relative to the position of the sun.

Chapter Review Games and Activities

CHAPTER
5

For use after Chapter 5

Math Riddle

Complete the following exercises. Find the answer to each exercise in the column at the right. Place the letter of the correct answer on the line above the appropriate exercise number. When you fill in the letters for all eight exercises, you will answer the following question.

What kind of tree does a math teacher climb?

Exercises

1. Simplify $\dfrac{(3x^{-2}y^3)^4}{36xy^6}$.

2. Evaluate $f(x) = -x^4 - 3x^2 - 4x + 5$ when $x = -2$.

3. Add $3x^3 - 5x^2 + 1$ and $x^2 + 4x - 6$.

4. Multiply $(x - 3)$, $(x + 5)$, and $(x - 1)$.

5. Factor $3x^4 + 9x^3 - 12x^2$.

6. Solve $2x^5 + 18x = 20x^3$.

7. Divide $4x^4 - 3x^3 - 2x^2 + 6x + 10$ by $x^2 + 5$.

8. Find all real zeros of $f(x) = x^3 - 19x + 30$.

Answers

(A) $4x^3 - x^2 - 5$

(T) $x = 3, 1, 0, -1, -3$

(E) $f(x) = -15$

(L) $x = 3$

(G) $\dfrac{9y^6}{4x^9}$

(R) $4x^2 - 3x - 22 + \dfrac{21x + 120}{x^2 + 5}$

(S) $\dfrac{9xy}{4}$

(M) $x^3 + x^2 - 17x + 15$

(C) $f(x) = 17$

(O) $3x^3 - 4x^2 + 4x - 5$

(E) $3x^2(x + 4)(x - 1)$

(Y) $x = 3, 2, -5$

___ ___ ___ ___ ___ ___ ___ ___
 1   2   3   4   5   6   7   8

REVIEW AND PROJECT

Project: Playing the Game

CHAPTER 5

For use after Chapter 5

Objective Create a game that students can use to review polynomial functions.

Materials old games, construction paper, poster board, index cards, marking pens, rulers, scissors, tape or glue

Investigation Games are fun, but they can also be a great learning tool. In this project, you will design a game based on your study of polynomial functions.

1. Create a set of rules. Your game should require players to be familiar with as many concepts from Chapter 5 as possible.

2. If your game requires players to answer questions about polynomial functions, provide at least 10 questions and answers to use in your game. Otherwise, describe at least 10 different situations that a player would encounter that require knowledge of polynomial functions, and explain what the player should do in these situations.

3. Decide on a name and design the box for your game. Create or provide all of the pieces or equipment to play the game. These may include a game board, question cards with answers, pawns, dice, spinners, pencils, paper, and so on.

4. Test your game by playing it with other students in your class. Make adjustments, if necessary.

Present Your Results Write a brief report explaining how you designed your game. If you worked in a group, include a paragraph describing your personal contributions to the project. Do you think your game could be played by students in other classes that have studied polynomials? If you needed to design another game, what would you do differently?

Teacher's Notes for Playing the Game Project *continued*
For use after Chapter 5

Project Goals

• Write and answer various questions about polynomial functions.

Managing the Project

This project requires a lot of creativity, and the class presentations may take some time, so you may wish to have students work in groups.

Encourage groups to make collective decisions and to prepare the final report jointly. If necessary, you can break the report into parts and have each student write the first draft of one part.

Questions you may want to ask to motivate students include: What are the most important skills from this chapter? What are some applications of polynomials? What are the rules of your favorite board game?

If students seem confused about how to create a game, you may want to provide an example. The sample answer given in the back of this resource book may be used for this purpose.

Discuss reasons for variations, if any. Have a class discussion at the completion of the project.

Rubric for Project

The following rubric can be used to assess student work.

4 The rules and object of the game are clear. Knowledge of polynomial functions is required to successfully play the game, and the questions provided by the student are reasonable. The answers provided are correct. The game is well designed, fun to play, and presented in an appealing way.

3 The rules and object of the game are clear. Knowledge of polynomial functions is required to successfully play the game, but the questions provided by the student may not have been chosen correctly or the student may have made a few errors in answering the questions. The game is reasonably well designed and presented in an appealing way.

2 The game is playable, but work may be incomplete or reflect misunderstanding. For example, the rules may not have been explained adequately or many of the questions provided by the student may have been answered incorrectly. The report may indicate a limited grasp of key ideas.

1 Portions of the game are missing. The student who created the game does not demonstrate an understanding of polynomial functions, or players are not required to understand polynomial functions to play the game.

CHAPTER 5 Cumulative Review
For use after Chapter 5

Convert the rate into the given units. *(Lesson 1.1)*

1. 22 ft/sec to miles per hour

2. 99 km/h to meters per second

Evaluate the power. *(Lesson 1.2)*

3. 2^3

4. $(-1)^4$

5. $(1)^{12}$

Solve the inequality. Then graph your solution. *(Lesson 1.6)*

6. $2x + 3 > -3$

7. $4x + 4 \le 8$

Solve the equation. Check for extraneous solutions. *(Lesson 1.7)*

8. $|t + 15| = 2t$

9. $|5x - 3| = x + 3$

Tell whether the lines are *parallel, perpendicular,* or *neither*. *(Lesson 2.2)*

10. Line 1: through $(3, 2)$ and $(2, 1)$

Line 2: through $(0, 2)$ and $(-2, 0)$

11. Line 1: through $(4, 4)$ and $(2, 4)$

Line 2: through $(0, 1)$ and $(-1, 1)$

Find the *x*- and *y*-intercepts of the line with the given equation. *(Lesson 2.3)*

12. $2x - 3y = 5$

13. $3x - y = 1$

14. $-2x - y = 4$

Write and graph a direct variation equation that has the given ordered pair as a solution. *(Lesson 2.5)*

15. $(2, -5)$

16. $(-1, 4)$

17. Draw a scatter plot of the data, approximate the best-fitting line, and estimate y when $x = 12$. *(Lesson 2.6)*

x	−2	−1	1	3	4
y	−5	−2	3	8	11

Tell whether the given order pairs are solutions of the inequality. *(Lesson 2.8)*

18. $x - y \ge 2$; $(1, 3)$, $(3, 1)$

19. $2x + y \le 4$; $(2, -4)$, $(2, 1)$

20. **Currency** You have one dollar bills and five dollar bills totaling 45 dollars. You have 4 times as many one dollar bills as you do five dollar bills. How many of each type of bill do you have? *(Lesson 3.1)*

Solve the system using any algebraic method. *(Lessons 3.2, 3.4)*

21. $2x - y = 3$
$3x + 2y = 8$

22. $x - 2y = -8$
$3x + 2y = 0$

23. $2x - 5y + z = 0$
$3x - y - 2z = -7$
$4x + y + 3z = 2$

CHAPTER 5	**Cumulative Review** *continued*

For use after Chapter 5

Solve the matrix equation for *x* and *y*. *(Lesson 3.5)*

24. $\begin{bmatrix} 2 & 3 \\ 1 & 2 \end{bmatrix} + \begin{bmatrix} -4 & 2y \\ x & -2 \end{bmatrix} = \begin{bmatrix} -2 & 5 \\ 2 & 0 \end{bmatrix}$

25. $3x\begin{bmatrix} 1 & -2 \\ 2 & 4 \end{bmatrix} = \begin{bmatrix} 6 & -12 \\ 12 & 8y \end{bmatrix}$

Find the product. If it is not defined, state the reason. *(Lesson 3.6)*

26. $\begin{bmatrix} 2 & 4 \\ 2 & 1 \end{bmatrix}\begin{bmatrix} -1 & -3 \\ 2 & 1 \end{bmatrix}$

27. $\begin{bmatrix} 1 & -2 \\ 2 & 4 \end{bmatrix}\begin{bmatrix} 3 \\ 4 \end{bmatrix}$

Graph the function. Label the vertex and axis of symmetry. *(Lessons 4.1, 4.2)*

28. $y = x^2 - 4$

29. $y = -3x^2 - 9x + 6$

30. $y = (x - 1)^2$

31. $y = 2(x + 3)^2 - 6$

Factor the expression. If the expression cannot be factored, say so.
(Lessons 4.3, 4.4)

32. $g^2 - 3g + 2$

33. $h^2 - 5h + 18$

34. $4r^2 - 3r + 6$

35. $2q^2 - 5q + 3$

Solve the equation by completing the square. *(Lesson 4.7)*

36. $t^2 - 3t = 6$

37. $2c^2 + 3c - 5 = c + 2$

38. $f^2 - 4f = 5$

Evaluate the expression. Tell which property of exponents you used.
(Lesson 5.1)

39. $2^3 \cdot 2^5$

40. $\dfrac{4^5}{4^2}$

41. $(3^2)^3$

Use direct substitution to evaluate the polynomial function for the given value of *x*. *(Lesson 5.2)*

42. $f(x) = 3x^3 + x - 3; x = 2$

43. $f(x) = 2x^2 + 3x - 1; x = -1$

Factor the polynomial completely using any method. *(Lesson 5.4)*

44. $x^3 - 5x^2 + 8x - 4$

45. $4x^4 - 32x$

46. $2x^3 + 6x^2 - 5x - 15$

Find all the real zeros of the function. *(Lesson 5.6)*

47. $f(x) = 2x^3 + 3x^2 + 14x + 21$

48. $f(x) = x^3 + 5x^2 - 13x + 7$

Graph the function. *(Lesson 5.8)*

49. $f(x) = (x + 2)^2(x - 1)$

50. $f(x) = 2(x - 2)^2(x + 2)^2$

Write a cubic function whose graph passes through the points. *(Lesson 5.9)*

51. $(-2, 0), (0, 0), (1, 0), (-1, 2)$

52. $(-1, -2), (0, 2), (1, 2), (2, 4)$

Answers

Lesson 5.1

Teaching Guide

1. $-2: 3$ **2.** $81; 9; 729; 729$ **3.** $25; 125; 3125;$ 3125 **4.** It is equivalent to the base raised to the sum of the two exponents. **5.** A way to write numbers using powers of 10 having the form $c \times 10^n$ where $1 \le c < 10$ and n is an integer; $6.4 \times 10^7; 3.4 \times 10^{-4}$

Investigating Algebra Activity

1. a. $(6 \cdot 6 \cdot 6 \cdot 6)(6 \cdot 6 \cdot 6 \cdot 6 \cdot 6 \cdot 6 \cdot 6); 6^{11}$
b. $(3 \cdot 3 \cdot 3 \cdot 3)(3 \cdot 3 \cdot 3 \cdot 3)(3 \cdot 3 \cdot 3 \cdot 3); 3^{12}$

c. $\dfrac{5 \cdot 5 \cdot 5 \cdot 5 \cdot 5 \cdot 5 \cdot 5 \cdot 5}{5 \cdot 5 \cdot 5 \cdot 5} = 5 \cdot 5 \cdot 5 \cdot 5; 5^4$

d. $\dfrac{4}{7} \cdot \dfrac{4}{7} \cdot \dfrac{4}{7} \cdot \dfrac{4}{7} \cdot \dfrac{4}{7} = \dfrac{4 \cdot 4 \cdot 4 \cdot 4 \cdot 4}{7 \cdot 7 \cdot 7 \cdot 7 \cdot 7}; \dfrac{4^5}{7^5}$

2. See answers to Exercise 1. **3.** For the product of powers property, the exponents in the *Simplified form* column are the sum of the exponents in the *Exponential expression* column. For the power of a power property, the exponents in the *Simplified form* column are the product of the exponents in the *Exponential expression* column. For the quotient of powers property, the exponents in the *Simplified form* column are the difference of the exponents in the *Exponential expression* column. For the power of a quotient property, the exponent in the *Exponential expression* column is applied to the numerator and denominator to give the expression in the *Simplified form* column. **4.** *Sample answer:* The product of powers property means that if you are multiplying like bases, the exponents will be added. The power of a power property means that if you are raising a power to a power, the exponents will be multiplied. The quotient of a power property means that if you are dividing like bases, the exponents will be subtracted. The power of a quotient property means that if you are raising a quotient to a power, you will raise both the numerator and denominator to that power.

Practice Level A

1. 9 **2.** 125 **3.** 32 **4.** 256 **5.** 1 **6.** $\dfrac{1}{2}$

7. $\dfrac{1}{49}$ **8.** $\dfrac{1}{1,000,000}$ **9–20.** Check properties.

9. 1024 **10.** -243 **11.** $15,625$ **12.** 1

13. $\dfrac{1}{32}$ **14.** 27 **15.** $1,000,000,000$ **16.** $\dfrac{25}{36}$

17. -3125 **18.** $\dfrac{1}{8}$ **19.** 6561 **20.** 32

21. 5.27×10^5 **22.** 5.26×10^{-5} **23.** 2.3×10^3

24. 5.983×10^{12} **25.** 1.76×10^{16}

26. 7.0×10^{-7} **27.** 4.8×10^9 **28.** 3.534×10^3

29. 7.84×10^6 **30.** 1.849×10^5 **31.** 6.0×10^2

32. 7.5×10^1 **33–40.** Check properties.

33. b^6 **34.** x^2 **35.** s^{14} **36.** $25y^2$ **37.** z^4

38. $\dfrac{1}{m^4}$ **39.** $\dfrac{x^3}{27}$ **40.** $\dfrac{16}{n^2}$ **41.** 3.26×10^8

42. about 2.65×10^4 dollars

Practice Level B

1–8. Check properties. **1.** 256 **2.** -343

3. $\dfrac{1}{16,384}$ **4.** $\dfrac{1}{625}$ **5.** $\dfrac{1}{256}$ **6.** $\dfrac{1}{262,144}$ **7.** $\dfrac{8}{27}$

8. $\dfrac{125}{64}$ **9.** 1.342×10^{12} **10.** 3.38×10^{-5}

11. 1.054×10^{-2} **12.** 4.698×10^6

13. 2.025×10^9 **14.** 1.369×10^{-9}

15. 3.73248×10^{-7} **16.** 6.6×10^1

17. 3.5×10^{-15} **18–29.** Check properties.

18. x^4 **19.** y^{11} **20.** $531,441s^{18}$

21. $\dfrac{1}{w^{10}}$ **22.** $\dfrac{y}{z^3}$ **23.** $\dfrac{16m^7}{n^3}$ **24.** $\dfrac{1}{49c^{14}d^4}$

25. $\dfrac{h^9}{125g^{12}}$ **26.** $\dfrac{1}{y^2}$ **27.** $4q^3r$ **28.** $\dfrac{4b^{14}}{7a^5}$

29. $\dfrac{4f^3}{9e^5}$ **30.** $S = \dfrac{4}{9}\pi x^2$ **31.** $V = \dfrac{4}{3}\pi x^4$

32. $V = \dfrac{32}{3}\pi x^6$ **33.** about 1.03×10^{11}

34. about 6.1×10^1

Practice Level C

1–8. Check properties. **1.** 25 **2.** 2187

3. 1024 **4.** 256 **5.** $\dfrac{64}{27}$ **6.** 729 **7.** $\dfrac{512}{19,683}$

8. $\dfrac{1}{125}$ **9.** 2.139×10^5 **10.** 9.72×10^{-6}

11. 1.6×10^5 **12.** 2.0×10^{-3} **13.** 1.0×10^{-6}

14. 2.5×10^1 **15–22.** Check properties. **15.** x^6

16. $-\dfrac{2m^7}{n^6}$ **17.** $\dfrac{45c^{13}}{d^5}$ **18.** 1 **19.** $\dfrac{9}{x^{14}y^2}$ **20.** $\dfrac{27r^6}{q^3s^3}$

21. $\dfrac{1}{z^{12}}$ **22.** b^{18} **23.** *Sample answer:* $a^4b^4c^5$

24. *Sample answer:* $6x^3y^4z$ **25.** *Sample answer:* $16m^6n^{17}$ **26.** about 1.665×10^{25} **27. a.** $\dfrac{2}{3}$ **b.** $\dfrac{\pi}{6}$

c. *Sample answer:* The designer should choose the package shaped like a cube. There is more empty air space around the ornament to offer more protection from damage. Also, the cubic packages would fit more efficiently in a box for shipping.

Study Guide

1. $(2^2 \cdot 5)^3 = (2^2)^3 \cdot 5^3$ Power of a product

$\quad\quad\quad\quad = 2^6 \cdot 5^3$ Product of a power

$\quad\quad\quad\quad = 64 \cdot 125$ Evaluate power.

$\quad\quad\quad\quad = 8000$ Multiply.

2. $7^3 \cdot 7^{-1} = 7^2$ Product of powers

$\quad\quad\quad\quad = 49$ Evaluate power.

3. $(8^0 \cdot 6^{-2})^{-1} = 8^0 \cdot 6^2$ Power of a product

$\quad\quad\quad\quad = 1 \cdot 6^2$ Zero exponent

$\quad\quad\quad\quad = 36$ Evaluate power.

4. $\left(\dfrac{9^6}{9^4}\right)^3 = (9^2)^3$ Quotient of powers

$\quad\quad\quad\quad = 9^6$ Power of a power

$\quad\quad\quad\quad = 531{,}441$ Evaluate power.

5. 2.5515×10^{10} or about $25{,}515{,}000{,}000$ lb

6. $t^7 t^2 t^{-8} = t$ Product of powers

7. $(k^{-3}m^4)^{-2} = k^6 m^{-8}$ Power of a power

$\quad\quad\quad\quad = \dfrac{k^6}{m^8}$ Negative exponent

8. $\left(\dfrac{f^5}{g^{-2}}\right)^{-3} = \dfrac{f^{-15}}{g^6}$ Power of a quotient

$\quad\quad\quad\quad = \dfrac{1}{f^{15}g^6}$ Negative exponent

9. $\left(\dfrac{3x}{z^2}\right)^0 = 1$ Zero exponent

10. about 27 times

Real-Life Application

1. a. 1.496×10^8 km   **b.** 9.3×10^7 mi   **2.** yes

3. $111{,}458$ days   **4.** $\dfrac{39.507}{0.387} \approx 102$ **5.** 102 in.

6.

Planet	P	a
Mercury	2.41×10^{-1}	3.87×10^{-1}
Venus	6.15×10^{-1}	7.23×10^{-1}
Earth	1.00×10^0	1.00×10^0
Mars	1.881×10^0	1.523×10^0
Jupiter	1.1861×10^1	5.203×10^0
Saturn	2.9457×10^1	9.541×10^0
Uranus	8.4008×10^1	1.9190×10^1
Neptune	1.64784×10^2	3.0086×10^1
Pluto	2.4835×10^2	3.9507×10^1

Challenge Practice

1. $x^{n^2} y^{2n^2}$ **2.** $x^{2n+1} + y^{2-n}$ **3.** $\dfrac{y^{6n+2}}{x^{2n+4}}$

4. $x^{n+4} y^{n-2}$ **5.** negative   **6.** positive

7. positive   **8.** positive

9. a. Let $n = -k$. Then you have the following:

$$(a^m)^n = (a^m)^{-k} = \frac{1}{(a^m)^k} = \frac{1}{a^{km}} = a^{-mk} = a^{mn}.$$

b. Let $m = -k$. Then you have the following:

$$(a^m)^n = (a^{-k})^n = \left(\frac{1}{a^k}\right)^n = \frac{1^n}{a^{kn}} = \frac{1}{a^{kn}} = a^{-kn} = a^{mn}.$$

c. Let $m = -p$ and let $n = -q$. Then you have the following:

$$(a^m)^n = (a^{-p})^{-q} = \left(\frac{1}{a^p}\right)^{-q} = a^{pq} = a^{(-m)(-n)} = a^{mn}.$$

d. Work with each side separately. For $n = 0$, $(a^m)^n = (a^m)^0 = 1$ and $a^{mn} = a^{m \cdot 0} = a^0 = 1$.

10. a. $v = \sqrt{\dfrac{2GM}{r}}$ **b.** $v \approx 11{,}174$ m/sec;

The initial velocity is less than the escape velocity, so the rocket will not travel infinitely into space. **c.** When the equation is solved for v, the variable m representing the mass of the projectile divides out, so no matter the mass of the projectile, the velocity of the projectile launched from Earth needed to travel infinitely into space is about $11{,}174$ m/sec.

ANSWERS

Lesson 5.2

Teaching Guide

1. $y = ax^2 + bx + c$, where $a \neq 0$; a polynomial function whose terms are written in descending order of exponents from left to right

2. 1; none; 2; one; when graphing quadratics we choose points on both sides of the vertex

3. The number of possible turning points will also increase. We can determine the slope for that interval. It helps to analyze the graph.

Practice Level A

1. yes; $f(x) = 5x + 2$ **2.** no

3. yes; $g(x) = 3x^2 + x + 15$

4. yes; $h(x) = \frac{1}{2}x^4 + 3x^3 - x^2$

5. 2; quadratic; 2 **6.** 1; linear; -3

7. 4; quartic; 2 **8.** 3; cubic; $\sqrt{2}$ **9.** 9 **10.** 31

11. 1 **12.** -44 **13.** 0 **14.** -99 **15.** B

16. C **17.** A **18. a.** 3; cubic **b.** 100, 490, 680, 820, 1060

c.

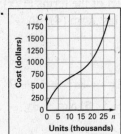

Practice Level B

1. yes; $f(x) = -2x + 7$; 1; linear; -2

2. yes; $g(x) = -x^3 + 2x + 8$; 3; cubic; -1

3. no **4.** 24 **5.** -283 **6.** 93 **7.** 3

8. $+\infty, -\infty$ **9.** $-\infty, +\infty$

10. $+\infty, +\infty$ **11.** $-\infty, -\infty$

12.

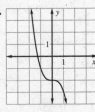

13.

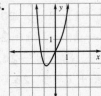

14.

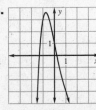

15. a. $S(t) \to -\infty$ as $t \to -\infty$ and $S(t) \to -\infty$ as $t \to +\infty$

b.

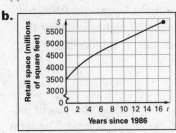

c. 1996 **d.** about 5715 million ft^2; *Sample answer:* No. The function starts to decrease after 2007, and the amount of retail space will probably continue to increase over time.

Practice Level C

1. yes; $f(x) = x^3\sqrt{5} - 2x^2 + 7$; 3; cubic; $\sqrt{5}$

2. no **3.** 32 **4.** 275 **5.** *Sample answer:* $f(x) = x^5 - x$; When a polynomial function has several missing terms, it is easier and much quicker to use direct substitution rather than synthetic substitution. **6.** $+\infty, -\infty$

7. $-\infty, +\infty$ **8.** $+\infty, +\infty$ **9.** $-\infty, -\infty$

10.

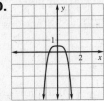

11.

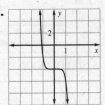

12.

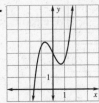

13. *Sample answer:* $f(x) = -x^4 + 2x^3$

14. a. about 6 in.

b.

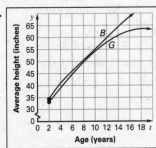

c. *Sample answer:* Female; According to the models, the average 14-year-old male is about 64 inches, and the average 14-year-old female is about 61 inches. Because 60 inches is closer to 61 inches than to 64 inches, it is more likely the 14-year-old is female.

Study Guide

1. not a polynomial; The leading coefficient is not a real number. **2.** not a polynomial; The term x^{-1} has an exponent that is not a whole number.

3. is a polynomial already in standard form with degree 2 (quadratic) and leading coefficient of 3π

4. -30 **5.** $f(x) \rightarrow +\infty$ as $x \rightarrow -\infty$; $f(x) \rightarrow +\infty$ as $x \rightarrow +\infty$ **6.** $f(x) \rightarrow -\infty$ as $x \rightarrow -\infty$; $f(x) \rightarrow +\infty$ as $x \rightarrow +\infty$

Problem Solving Workshop: Worked Out Example

1.

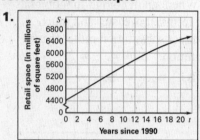

about $6{,}500{,}000{,}000$ ft^2

2.

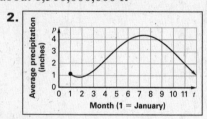

July, August

Challenge Practice

1. a. 3 **b.** 3.36 **c.** 3.75 **d.** 3.99 **e.** 3.9975
2. The average rate of change seems to be approaching 4.
3. a. $y = 3x - 3$ **b.** $y = 3.36x - 3.36$
c. $y = 3.75x - 3.75$ **d.** $y = 3.99x - 3.99$
e. $y = 3.9975x - 3.9975$ **4.** $y = 4x - 4$

Lesson 5.3

Teaching Guide

1. $2x^2 - 11x + 9$ **2.** $5x^2 + 5x - 18$
3. $6x^2 + 3x + 5$ **4.** $x^2 - 11x + 30$
5. $3x^2 + 31x + 36$ **6.** $6x^2 - x - 40$

Investigating Algebra Activity

1. a. $(2x + 3)(2x + 3)$; $4x^2 + 6x + 6x + 9$; $4x^2 + 12x + 9$ **b.** $(4x + 5y)(4x + 5y)$; $16x^2 + 20xy + 20xy + 25y^2$; $16x^2 + 40xy + 25y^2$
c. $(x - y)(x - y)$; $x^2 - xy - xy + y^2$; $x^2 - 2xy + y^2$ **d.** $(2x - 3)(2x - 3)$; $4x^2 - 6x - 6x + 9$; $4x^2 - 12x + 9$;
e. $(4x - 5y)(4x - 5y)$; $16x^2 - 20xy - 20xy + 25y^2$; $16x^2 - 40xy + 25y^2$

2. The first term in the simplified expression is the square of the first term of the binomial.

3. The last term in the simplified expression is the square of the last term of the binomial.

4. The second term in the simplified expression is twice the product of the terms of the binomial.

5. If the operation in the binomial is addition, then the operations in the simplified expression are addition. If the operation in the binomial is subtraction, then the first operation in the simplied expression is subtraction and the second is addition. **6.** *Sample answer:* To square a binomial like $(3x - 2)$, square the first term $(9x^2)$; then subtract twice the product of the terms $(12x)$; finally, add the square of the last term (4). So, $(3x - 2)^2 = 9x^2 - 12x + 4$

Practice Level A

1. $6x^3 - x^2 + 3x - 9$ **2.** $2x^3 - 8x^2 - 8x + 9$
3. $3x^2 + 5x + 16$ **4.** $5x^2 - 3$ **5.** $6x^2 - 3x$
6. $4b^2 - b + 6$ **7.** $15n^2 - 3n - 1$
8. $15m^3 + 2m^2 + 2m + 9$
9. $-5w^3 + 4w^2 - 5w - 3$
10. $2x^3 + 13$ **11.** $8c^2 - 2c - 9$
12. $4y^2 - 9y + 7$ **13.** $-z^3 + 4z^2 + 5z + 1$
14. $8x^3 + 8x^2 - 13x + 1$
15. $6t^4 - t^3 + 2t^2 - 3t + 18$ **16.** $2x^3 + 3x^2 - x$
17. $8y^4 - 32y^3$ **18.** $m^2 + 5m - 6$
19. $c^2 - 11c + 18$ **20.** $8z^2 + 3z - 5$
21. $h^3 - h^2 - 14h + 24$ **22.** $x^2 - 49$
23. $s^2 + 18s + 81$ **24.** $x^2 - 4x + 4$
25. $2x^2 + x - 3$ **26.** $3x^2 - 7x + 2$
27. $Y = -0.01975t^4 + 0.2309t^3 - 0.44t^2 + 2.27t + 263$

Practice Level B

1. $3y^2 - 6y - 3$ **2.** $x^2 + 9x - 8$
3. $5m^3 - 4m^2 + 9m - 3$

4. $7s^4 - 2s^3 - 8s^2 + s + 7$

5. $-11q^3 + 5q^2 + 6q + 16$

6. $-3z^4 - z^3 + 3z^2 + 6z + 2$

7. $8v^4 + 6v^3 - 2v^2 + v - 16$

8. $5x^5 + x^4 - x^3 - 5x$ **9.** $10x^4 - 2x^3$

10. $w^2 - 9w + 8$ **11.** $c^2 + 14c + 40$

12. $g^2 + 7g - 18$ **13.** $y^3 + 5y^2 - 8y + 2$

14. $2n^3 + 9n^2 - 12n - 35$ **15.** $x^2 - 6x + 9$

16. $16t^2 + 8t + 1$ **17.** $z^3 - 15z^2 + 75z - 125$

18. $8f^3 + 12f^2 + 6f + 1$ **19.** $2x^3 + 13x^2 + 6x$

20. $\frac{1}{3}\pi x^3 - \pi x^2 - 3\pi x + 9\pi$

21. $C = 315t^3 + 25,060t^2 + 71,923t + 1,967,822$; about 4,308,326 thousand gallons

Practice Level C

1. $w^3 + 2w^2 + 6w - 9$

2. $-x^4 - 3x^3 + 2x^2 + 3x$

3. $4m^4 + 2m^3 - 2m^2 + 7m - 6$

4. $b^4 - 4b^3 - 6b^2 + 11b - 5$

5. $\frac{3}{5}x^3 - 7x - \frac{1}{3}$ **6.** $-\frac{1}{12}c^3 - 3c^2 + 5c + \frac{1}{6}$

7. $-\sqrt{2}\,d^2 - 7d + 9$ **8.** $8x^3 - 2\sqrt{3}\,x^2 - x$

9. $-6x^6 + 8x^5 - 2x^4$ **10.** $30s^2 + 7s - 2$

11. $12p^3 + 4p^2 + 15p + 8$

12. $-x^4 - 6x^3 + 5x^2 + 18x - 6$

13. $2x^7 + 6x^6 - 3x^5 + 3x^4 + x$

14. $x^6 + x^5 - 2x^4 - 6x^3 + x^2 + 10x - 5$

15. $-40q^3 + 149q^2 + 46q - 8$

16. $4x^2 - y^2$ **17.** $8y^3 + 36y^2z + 54yz^2 + 27z^3$

18. $\frac{1}{4}x^2 - \frac{1}{4}xy + \frac{1}{16}y^2$ **19.** $11x^2 - 2x - 2$

20. a. $A = -0.089t^5 - 2.19t^4 + 35.35t^3 - 151.8t^2 + 280t + 1904$ **b.** Because P represents a percent, it must be divided by 100 before multiplying it by F to get the model for the average annual amount spent on food away from home A. **c.** about \$2133

Study Guide

1. $3x^3 - 3x^2 + 4x + 3$ **2.** $7x^2 - 9x + 7$

3. $z^3 - 6z^2 + 8z - 3$ **4.** $x^3 - 7x + 6$

5. $x^3 + 6x^2 + 12x + 8$ **6.** $49y^2 - 28y + 4$

7. $16d^2 - 9$ **8.** $4a^2 + 20a + 25$

9. $V = \pi(x^3 + 7x^2 + 16x + 12)$; 36π

Real-Life Application

1. Triangular-base pyramid: 4, 10, 20, 35, 56, 84, 120, 165, 220, 286, 364; Square-base pyramid: 5, 14, 30, 55, 91, 140, 204, 285, 385, 506, 650

2.

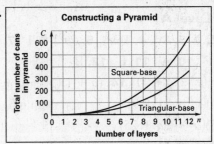

Constructing a Pyramid

The graph of the square-base pyramid goes higher than the graph of the triangular-base pyramid, which means the square-base pyramid has more cans than the triangular-base pyramid.

3. $\frac{1}{6}n^3 + n^2 + \frac{11}{6}n + 1$

4. Find the difference between $\frac{1}{6}n^3 + n^2 + \frac{11}{6}n + 1$ and $\frac{1}{6}n^3 + \frac{1}{2}n^2 + \frac{1}{3}n$; $\frac{1}{2}n^2 + \frac{3}{2}n + 1$.

5. $\frac{1}{3}n^3 + \frac{3}{2}n^2 + \frac{13}{6}n + 1$

6. Find the difference between $\frac{1}{3}n^3 + \frac{3}{2}n^2 + \frac{13}{6}n + 1$ and $\frac{1}{3}n^3 + \frac{1}{2}n^2 + \frac{1}{6}n$; $n^2 + 2n + 1$.

7. 1330 cans **8.** 356 cans

Challenge Practice

1. $15x^{3r} + 12x^{4r-1}$ **2.** $20x^{2r+2} - 15x^{2r}$

3. $12x^{3m} - 10x^{2m} - 18x^m + 15$

4. $2x^{7m} - 2x^{6m} + x^{5m} - x^{4m}$

5. $a^2 + b^2 + c^2 + 2ab + 2ac + 2bc$

6. a. $x^4 + 6x^3 + 5x^2 - 12x + 4$

b. $16x^2 + 25y^2 + 56x - 70y - 40xy + 49$

7. $(x + a)^2 = x^2 + 2ax + a^2$; square of a binomial

8. $(x + a)(x + b) = x^2 + bx + ax + ab$; FOIL method

9. a. Carey: $500r^3 + 2300r^2 + 3700r + 1900$; Emma: $750r^3 + 2750r^2 + 4150r + 2150$

b. $1250r^3 + 5050r^2 + 7850r + 4050$ **c.** Emma's account is worth more.

Lesson 5.4

Teaching Guide

1. $(x)(x + 8)(x - 2) = 96$; The factors should be set to zero in order to use the zero product property.

Lesson 5.4, continued

2. $x^3 + 6x^2 - 16x - 96 = 0$

3. $x^2(x + 6)$; $-16(x + 6)$; both have $(x + 6)$ as a factor **4.** $(x + 4)(x - 4)(x + 6) = 0$; 4, -4, and -6; 4; 12 cm by 2 cm by 4 cm

Practice Level A

1. $4x^3$ **2.** 2 **3.** $8x$ **4.** $16n^2$ **5.** $5p^2$ **6.** 1 **7.** C

8. D **9.** F **10.** A **11.** E **12.** B

13. $(s - 1)(s^2 + s + 1)$ **14.** $(q + 1)(q^2 - q + 1)$

15. $(x - 3)(x^2 + 3x + 9)$

16. $(a + 5)(a^2 - 5a + 25)$

17. $(h + 4)(h^2 - 4h + 16)$

18. $(2y - 5)(4y^2 + 10y + 25)$

19. $(x^2 + 3)(x + 2)$ **20.** $(z^2 + 5)(z - 1)$

21. $(f^2 + 1)(f + 4)$ **22.** $(m^2 + 4)(m - 2)$

23. $(x^2 + 3)(2x - 1)$ **24.** $(t - 2)(t + 3)(t - 3)$

25. 0, 3 **26.** -5, 0 **27.** 2, 3 **28.** -4, 4

29. 0, 3 **30.** -3, -1, 3 **31.** C **32.** A **33.** B

Practice Level B

1. $(x + 5)(x^2 - 5x + 25)$

2. $(y - 2)(y^2 + 2y + 4)$

3. $(4n - 3)(16n^2 + 12n + 9)$

4. $(3g + 7)(9g^2 - 21g + 49)$

5. $2(w + 3)(w^2 - 3w + 9)$

6. $5(2v - 5)(4v^2 + 10v + 25)$

7. $(r^2 + 6)(r - 3)$ **8.** $(x^2 + 7)(x + 6)$

9. $(c + 3)(c - 3)(c + 4)$

10. $(z + 4)(z - 4)(z - 2)$

11. $(5p + 1)(5p - 1)(p - 1)$

12. $(3m + 2)(3m - 2)(m + 2)$

13. $(x^2 - 6)(x^2 + 6)$ **14.** $(c + 3)(c - 3)(c^2 + 9)$

15. $(x + 2)(x - 2)(x^2 + 5)$

16. $(2y^3 + 1)(3y^3 - 4)$ **17.** $(x^3 + 2)(x^3 - 2)$

18. $(d^2 - 5)(d^2 - 2)$

19. $3(2q - 3)(4q^2 + 6q + 9)$

20. $(a^3 + 6)(a + 1)(a^2 - a + 1)$

21. $-2(2x^2 - 3)(x^2 - 5)$

22. $2(b + 7)(b - 2)(b^2 + 2b + 4)$ **23.** -6, 0

24. $0, \frac{9}{4}$ **25.** -5, -2, 5 **26.** $-5, -\sqrt{3}, \sqrt{3}$

27. $-3, -\sqrt{5}, \sqrt{5}, 3$ **28.** -1, 0, 1

29. Sample answer: $x^6 - 1$; $(x + 1)(x - 1)(x^2 + x + 1)(x^2 - x + 1)$

Algebra 2

30. 6 ft by 3 ft by 1 ft

Practice Level C

1. $(x - 8)(x^2 + 8x + 64)$

2. $2(a + 6)(a^2 - 6a + 36)$

3. $7(h + 4)(h^2 - 4h + 16)$

4. $-3(c - 2)(c^2 + 2c + 4)$

5. $(6x^2 + 1)(2x - 1)$ **6.** $(3k^3 - 7)(k + 9)$

7. $(n + 4)(n - 4)(3n - 10)$

8. $x^3(x + 1)^2(x - 1)$ **9.** $(y^2 + 9)(y + 3)(y - 3)$

10. $2(z^2 + 25)(z + 5)(z - 5)$

11. $(3a^2 - 1)(2a^2 + 5)$

12. $(6b^2 + 7)(b + 2)(b - 2)$

13. $(r - 1)(r^2 + r + 1)(r^2 + 1)$

14. $-4w^2(w^2 + 2)(w^2 + 1)(w + 1)(w - 1)$

15. $(a^2b + 5)(a^4b^2 - 5a^2b + 25)$

16. $(c^2 - d^2)(2a - 5b)$ **17.** -10 **18.** $\frac{2}{3}$ **19.** 4

20. -4, -3, 3 **21.** $-\frac{3}{5}, 1$ **22.** $-\sqrt{7}, -2, 2, \sqrt{7}$

23. $-\frac{1}{3}, \frac{1}{3}$ **24.** -2, 2 **25.** -1, 0, 1

26. $-1, -\frac{3}{4}, \frac{3}{4}, 1$ **27.** $-\frac{\sqrt{6}}{2}, 0, \frac{\sqrt{6}}{2}$ **28.** $0, \frac{3}{2}$

29. Sample answer:
$x^4 + 5x^3 + x + 5$; $(x + 5)(x + 1)(x^2 - x + 1)$

30. a. $V_1 = 36\pi x^3$, $V_2 = 16\pi x^3$, $V_3 = 4\pi x^3$

b. $56\pi x^3 = 448\pi$ **c.** 2 **d.** level 1: 12 ft, 2 ft; level 2: 8 ft, 2 ft; level 3: 4 ft, 2 ft

Study Guide

1. $7x^2(x - 2)(x^2 + 2x + 4)$

2. $2(4y^2 + 1)(16y^4 - 4y^2 + 1)$

3. $(x + 2)(x - 2)(x - 3)$

4. $(y - 3)(y + 3)(y + 7)$ **5.** $3b^2(b^2 + 1)^2$

6. $(z^2 + 4)(z^2 + 2)(z^2 - 2)$ **7.** $\pm 1, \pm\sqrt{2}$

8. $0, \pm\sqrt{6}, \pm\sqrt{2}$ **9.** $0, \pm\sqrt{3}, \pm 3$

10. 8 in. by 3 in. by 1 in.

Interdisciplinary Application

1. 18,750 gal **2.** Aquarium 1: $x^3 - 96x^2 + 2304x - 41,472 = 0$; 72 in. by 24 in. by 24 in.; Aquarium 2: $x^3 - 11.5x^2 + 33x - 40 = 0$; 8 ft by 2 ft by 2.5 ft; Aquarium 3: $3x^3 + 12x^2 - 28,800 = 0$; 60 in. by 24 in. by 20 in.

Lesson 5.4, continued

Challenge Practice

1. $(2y^n + 1)(2y^n - 3)$ **2.** $(3x^n + 2)(x^n - 6)$

3. $2(x^n + 2y^n)(x^{2n} - 2x^ny^n + 4y^{2n})$

4. The polynomial is already completely factored. **5.** $(a^2 + b^2)(-a^3b + 4b - 2ab + 1)$

6. $(2a^2 - b^3)(3ab + a^2b^2 - 6b + 1)$

7. Sample answer: $x^3 - 4x^2 - 4x + 16 = 0$

8. Sample answer: $x^4 + 4x^3 - 9x^2 - 36x = 0$

9. Sample answer: $x^3 + 6x^2 - 5x - 30 = 0$

10. Sample answer: $x^4 - 5x^3 - 12x^2 + 60x = 0$

11. $(-2, 8)$, $(\sqrt{3}, 10 + \sqrt{3})$, $(-\sqrt{3}, 10 - \sqrt{3})$

12. $(-4, 331)$, $\left(-\frac{1}{2}, 2\right)$, $\left(\frac{1}{2}, \frac{5}{2}\right)$, $(4, 587)$

13. a. $V = \frac{16\pi}{3}r^3$ **b.** Domain of V: $r > 0$

c. radius = 3 ft, length = 12 ft

Lesson 5.5

Teaching Guide

1. 3105; 12; 258; 9 **2.** multiply 12 and 258, then add 9 **3.** quotient is 26 with a remainder of 3; The zero positions the 3 and 1 in the thousands and hundreds positions respectively. Without the placeholder, the dividend does not represent the correct number.

Practice Level A

1. $x + 2$, $2x^3 + x^2 - x + 10$, $2x^2 - 3x + 5$, 0

2. $x - 4$, $3x^3 - 10x^2 - 5$, $3x^2 + 2x + 8$, 27

3. $x - 5 + \frac{5}{x - 1}$ **4.** $x - \frac{11}{x + 2}$ **5.** $x - 3$

6. $x - 2 + \frac{4}{x + 5}$ **7.** $4x + 9 + \frac{32}{x - 4}$

8. $2x - 7 + \frac{26}{x + 3}$ **9.** $x + 2 + \frac{8}{x - 2}$

10. $x^2 + 4x - 3$ **11.** $x - 1$ **12.** $x - 2 + \frac{1}{x + 1}$

13. $x + 5$ **14.** $x - 9 + \frac{31}{x + 3}$ **15.** $x + 1 - \frac{11}{x + 4}$

16. $2x + 3$ **17.** $x^2 + x + 2 + \frac{4}{x - 1}$

18. $x - 2 - \frac{3}{x + 2}$ **19.** $x + 7$ **20.** $x - 2$

21. $x + 3$ **22.** 1000 workbooks

Practice Level B

1. $x + 7$ **2.** $x - 7 - \frac{13}{x + 5}$ **3.** $x^2 - 3x + 10$

4. $3x - 1 + \frac{8}{2x - 1}$ **5.** $8x + 5 + \frac{12x + 25}{x^2 - 3}$

6. $5x^2 + 17x + 31 + \frac{16x - 112}{x^2 - 3x + 4}$ **7.** $x + 3$

8. $x^2 - 2x + 6 + \frac{1}{x - 1}$ **9.** $x^2 - 5x - 1 - \frac{12}{x - 2}$

10. $2x^3 - 3x^2 + 3x - 3 + \frac{7}{x + 1}$

11. $2x^3 - 5x^2 + 6$

12. $x^3 + x^2 + 7x + 9 + \frac{96}{x - 7}$

13. $(x - 6)(x + 1)(x + 2)$

14. $(x - 10)(x - 4)(x + 2)$

15. $(x - 9)(x - 2)(x - 7)$ **16.** $(x + 5)(x - 3)^2$

17. $(x - 1)(2x + 3)(2x - 3)$

18. $(x + 4)(3x - 1)(x - 9)$ **19.** 2 **20.** $-9, 12$

21. $-5, -\frac{1}{2}$ **22.** $-\frac{2}{5}, \frac{1}{3}$ **23.** 5 **24.** $-\sqrt{5}, \sqrt{5}$

25. $x - 2$

26. Answers may vary depending on rounding.

$A = -0.001x^2 + 0.0823x - 6.8943 + \frac{1909}{3x + 267}$

Practice Level C

1. $2x^2 - 4x + 9 - \frac{28}{2x + 3}$

2. $5x^2 + 20 + \frac{8x + 71}{x^2 - 4}$ **3.** $\frac{1}{2}x + \frac{x + 5}{2(2x^2 - 1)}$

4. $3x^2 - 6x + 1$ **5.** $2x - \frac{9}{x^3 + x^2 - 5}$

6. $8x^2 - 8x + 34 - \frac{70x - 111}{x^2 + x - 3}$

7. $2x^2 - 8x + 28 - \frac{107}{x + 4}$

8. $6x^2 + 12x + 17 + \frac{34}{x - 2}$

9. $x^3 + 2x^2 - 8x + 20 - \frac{56}{x + 3}$

10. $3x^3 + 9x^2 + 26x + 84 + \frac{252}{x - 3}$

11. $2x^2 + 5x - 1$

12. $3x^4 + 3x^3 + 5x^2 + 5x + \frac{1}{x - 1}$

13. $(x - 5)(x + 3)(x + 11)$

14. $(x + 2)(2x + 5)(2x - 5)$

15. $(x - 4)(x + 2)(x^2 - 2x + 4)$

16. $(x + 7)(2x - 1)(2x^2 + 3)$

17. $(x + 1)^2(x - 4)(x^2 - x + 1)$

18. $(x - 6)(3x - 1)(2x^3 - 5)$ **19.** $-3, 9$

20. $-\frac{2}{3}, \frac{2}{3}$ **21.** $-\frac{3}{2}, \frac{1}{3}$ **22.** $-2 - \sqrt{5}, -2 + \sqrt{5}$

23. $-\frac{5 - \sqrt{17}}{2}, -\frac{5 + \sqrt{17}}{2}$ **24.** $1 \pm i\sqrt{7}$

25. a. $300x - 8x^3$ **b.** $P = 125x - 8x^3$
c. $-8x^3 + 125x - 187.5 = 0$; about 2.06 million televisions **d.** No. -4.56 is a solution of the equation that does make sense because the company cannot produce a negative number of televisions.

Study Guide

1. $2x^2 + 4x + 7 + \dfrac{10x + 6}{x^2 - x - 1}$ **2.** $x + 3$

3. $x^3 + 3x^2 - 2x + 1$

4. $-x^3 + 2x^2 + 5 - \dfrac{5}{x + 2}$

5. $(x - 3)(x + 1)(x - 1)$

6. $(x - 3)(x - 1)(x + 2)$

7. $(x - 3)(x - 1)(x - 2)$ **8.** $-1, 2$ **9.** $1, 2$

Problem Solving Workshop:
Mixed Problem Solving

1. a. 1.04×10^{10} **b.** about 7482 days or about 20.5 years **2. a.** $O(x) = 3x^3 + 12x^2$
b. $I(x) = 3x^3 - 2x^2 - 12x + 8$ **c.** The function $W(x)$ is created by subtracting $I(x)$ from $O(x)$.
d. $W(x) = 14x^2 + 12x - 8$; 568 in.^{3}

3. Answers will vary. **4.** 5 **5. a.** 4, quartic
b.

t	0	1	2	3
B	61,181	61,938	62,390	62,394

t	4	5	6	7
B	61,910	61,002	59,836	58,683

t	8	9	10
B	57,915	58,010	59,547

c.

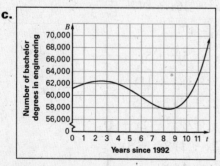

As $x \to +\infty$, $f(x) \to +\infty$. The number of bachelor degrees in 2012 will be more than the number of bachelor degrees in 2002 because the graph is increasing.

6. The surface area of the sun is about 3.39×10^5 greater than the surface area of Pluto.
7. a. $R = 120x - 12x^3$ **b.** $P = 96x - 12x^3$
c. -1, about 2.2 **d.** No; A negative value for produced DVD players does not make sense.

Challenge Practice

1.

$$
\begin{array}{r|rrrrr}
2 & 2 & 7 & -4 & -27 & -18 \\
  &   & 4 & 22 & 36 & 18 \\
\hline
  & 2 & 11 & 18 & 9 & 0
\end{array}
$$

$$
\begin{array}{r|rrrr}
-3 & 2 & 11 & 18 & 9 \\
   &   & -6 & -15 & -9 \\
\hline
   & 2 & 5 & 3 & 0
\end{array}
$$

So, $2x^2 + 5x + 3$ factors as $(2x + 3)(x + 1)$.

2.

$$
\begin{array}{r|rrrrr}
-2 & 8 & -14 & -71 & -10 & 24 \\
   &   & -16 & 60 & 22 & -24 \\
\hline
   & 8 & -30 & -11 & 12 & 0
\end{array}
$$

$$
\begin{array}{r|rrrr}
4 & 8 & -30 & -11 & 12 \\
  &   & 32 & 8 & -12 \\
\hline
  & 8 & 2 & -3 & 0
\end{array}
$$

So, $8x^2 + 2x - 3$ factors as $(4x + 3)(2x - 1)$.

3.

$$
\begin{array}{r|rrrrr}
1 & 2 & 1 & -75 & 107 & -35 \\
  &   & 2 & 3 & -72 & 35 \\
\hline
  & 2 & 3 & -72 & 35 & 0
\end{array}
$$

$$
\begin{array}{r|rrrr}
-7 & 2 & 3 & -72 & 35 \\
   &   & -14 & 77 & -35 \\
\hline
   & 2 & -11 & 5 & 0
\end{array}
$$

So, $2x^2 - 11x + 5$ factors as $(2x - 1)(x - 5)$.

Lesson 5.5, continued

4.

$$-8 \,\big|\; \begin{array}{ccccc} 12 & 19 & -588 & 236 & 96 \\ & -96 & 616 & -224 & -96 \\ \hline 12 & -77 & 28 & 12 & 0 \end{array}$$

$$6 \,\big|\; \begin{array}{cccc} 12 & -77 & 28 & 12 \\ & 72 & -30 & -12 \\ \hline 12 & -5 & -2 & 0 \end{array}$$

So, $12x^2 - 5x - 2$ factors as $(4x + 1)(3x - 2)$.

5. -210 **6.** 42 **7.** $x^{2n} + 6x^n + 9$

8. $x^{2n} - x^n + 3$ **9. a.** $x + 1$ **b.** $x^2 + x + 1$

c. $x^3 + x^2 + x + 1$

10. $\dfrac{x^n - 1}{x - 1} = x^{n-1} + x^{n-2} + \cdots + x^2 + x + 1$

11. Let the divisor $d(x)$ equal $(x - k)$. Now multiply each side of the equation $\dfrac{f(x)}{(x-k)} = q(x) + \dfrac{r(x)}{(x-k)}$ by $(x - k)$ to obtain $f(x) = (x - k)q(x) + r(x)$. Because either the remainder equals zero or the degree of the remainder is less than the degree of $(x - k)$, you know that the remainder must be a constant. That is $r(x) = r$. Now, by evaluating $f(x)$ at $x = k$, you have $f(k) = (k - k)q(k) + r = 0 \cdot q(x) + r = r$.

12. Let the divisor $d(x)$ equal $(x - k)$. Now multiply each side of the equation $\dfrac{f(x)}{(x-k)} = q(x) + \dfrac{r(x)}{(x-k)}$ by $(x - k)$ to obtain $f(x) = (x - k)q(x) + r(x)$. If $(x - k)$ is a factor of $f(x)$, division of $f(x)$ by $(x - k)$ yields a remainder of 0. So, by the remainder theorem, you have $f(k) = 0$. Conversely, by the remainder theorem, $r(x) = r = f(k)$, and you have $f(x) = (x - k)q(x) + f(k)$, where $q(x)$ is a polynomial of lesser degree than $f(x)$. If $f(k) = 0$, then $f(x) = (x - k)q(x)$ and you see that $(x - k)$ is a factor of $f(x)$.

Lesson 5.6

Teaching Guide

1. 2, 7; yes; $(7x - 1)(x + 3)$ **2.** zero product property **3.** The function's value is zero where the graph intersects the x-axis.; -3 and $\frac{1}{7}$

4. No; *Sample answer:* You can use the quadratic formula.

Practice Level A

1. No. The coefficients are not all integers.

2. $\pm 1, \pm 2, \pm 4, \pm 8, \pm 16$ **3.** $\pm 1, \pm 2, \pm 3, \pm 6,$ $\pm 9, \pm 18$ **4.** $\pm 1, \pm 2, \pm 3, \pm 4, \pm 6, \pm 8, \pm 12,$ ± 24 **5.** $\pm 1, \pm 2, \pm 4, \pm 5, \pm 10, \pm 20$

6. $\pm 1, \pm 3, \pm 9, \pm \frac{1}{2}, \pm \frac{3}{2}, \pm \frac{9}{2}$

7. $\pm 1, \pm 2, \pm 3, \pm 4, \pm 6, \pm 12, \pm \frac{1}{3}, \pm \frac{2}{3}, \pm \frac{4}{3}$

8. none **9.** $-3, -1, 3$ **10.** $-1, 1$ **11.** 1

12. $-3, -2, 4$ **13.** $-1, 1, 2$ **14.** $-3, 1, 10$

15. $-4, -1, 3$ **16.** $-2, 4, 5$ **17.** $-9, -2, 2$

18. $-1, 2$ **19.** $-2, -1, 2, 3$ **20.** $-5, -3, 1, 4$

21. $-3, -2, 1, 3$ **22. a.** $x^3 + 3x^2 = 54$ **b.** $\pm 1,$ $\pm 2, \pm 3, \pm 6, \pm 9, \pm 18, \pm 27, \pm 54$ **c.** 3

d. base: 3 in. by 3 in., height: 6 in.

Practice Level B

1. $\pm 1, \pm 3, \pm 7, \pm 21$ **2.** $\pm 1, \pm 2, \pm 3, \pm 5, \pm 6,$ $\pm 10, \pm 15, \pm 30, \pm \frac{1}{2}, \pm \frac{3}{2}, \pm \frac{5}{2}, \pm \frac{15}{2}$

3. $\pm 1, \pm 2, \pm 5, \pm 10, \pm \frac{1}{5}, \pm \frac{2}{5}$ **4.** $\pm 1, \pm 2, \pm 4,$

$\pm \frac{1}{9}, \pm \frac{2}{9}, \pm \frac{1}{3}, \pm \frac{4}{9}, \pm \frac{2}{3}, \pm \frac{4}{3}$ **5.** $-2, 1, 4$

6. $-4, -1, 1$ **7.** $-3, -2, 1$ **8.** $-5, -1, 1$

9. $-4, 3, 6$ **10.** $-\sqrt{2}, -1, \sqrt{2}$ **11.** $-\frac{3}{2}, \frac{1}{2}, 3$

12. $-\sqrt{2}, \sqrt{2}, \frac{5}{2}$ **13.** $-2, -1, 1$ **14.** $-2, \frac{1}{2}, 4$

15. $-\frac{3}{2}, \frac{1}{4}, 2$ **16.** $-1, 1$ **17.** $-3, -1, \frac{1}{2}, 1$

18. $-2, -\sqrt{2}, \sqrt{2}, \frac{1}{2}$

19. a. $t^4 - 18t^3 + 89t^2 - 32t - 400$

b. 1, 2, 4, 5, 8 **c.** 4; 1999

d. about 6.4 or 2001

Practice Level C

1. $-2, 1, 5$ **2.** $-3, 2$ **3.** $-3, -\sqrt{2}, -1, \sqrt{2}$

4. $-7, \dfrac{5 - \sqrt{21}}{2}, \dfrac{5 + \sqrt{21}}{2}$

5. $-3 - 2\sqrt{2}, -1, -3 + 2\sqrt{2}, 3$

6. $-5, -\sqrt{3}, \sqrt{3}$ **7.** $-3, 1, -\dfrac{1 + \sqrt{17}}{4}, -\dfrac{1 - \sqrt{17}}{4}$

8. $-3, -\frac{7}{2}, -\frac{1}{3}, 1$ **9.** $-\frac{3}{4}, -\frac{1}{2}, \frac{1}{3}, 2$

10. $-\frac{5}{2}, -\frac{3}{2}, \frac{1}{2}$ **11.** $-\dfrac{5 - \sqrt{17}}{4}, -1, -\dfrac{2}{3}, -\dfrac{5 + \sqrt{17}}{4}$

12. $-\dfrac{5}{2}, -\dfrac{1-\sqrt{13}}{6}, -\dfrac{1+\sqrt{13}}{6}, \dfrac{1}{2}$

13. $-\sqrt{3}, -\dfrac{5}{3}, \dfrac{1}{2}, \sqrt{3}$

14. $-4, 2-\sqrt{7}, -\dfrac{1}{2}, \dfrac{2}{3}, 2+\sqrt{7}$

15. *Sample answer:*
$f(x) = 6x^3 - 7x^2 + 10x + 2$

16. a. The function f has no constant term.

b. $x(2x^3 + 5x^2 - 21x - 36)$ **c.** $-4, -\dfrac{3}{2}, 0, 3$

d. $-\sqrt{2}, 0, \dfrac{1}{3}, \sqrt{2}$

17. a. for each function: $-5, -1, 4$ **b.** The zeros of $f(x)$ are also the zeros of $af(x)$. **c.** To apply the rational zero theorem, the coefficients must be integers.

d. $-3, -\dfrac{1}{4}, 1$

Study Guide

1. $-2, -1, 2$ **2.** $-4, -1, 3$ **3.** $-\dfrac{1}{2}, 1, 2$

4. $-1, 1, 3$ **5.** $-2, 1, 3$ **6.** $1, 2, 3$

7. $3 = \dfrac{1}{3}x^2(x-2)$; $\pm 1, \pm 3, \pm 9$; When $x = 3$, the sides have length 3 and the height is 1.

8. $24 = \dfrac{1}{2}x(x-1)x$; $\pm 1, \pm 2, \pm 3$; $\pm 4, \pm 6, \pm 8$, $\pm 12, \pm 16, \pm 24, \pm 48$; When $x = 4$, the dimensions are 2 in. by 3 in. by 4 in.

Problem Solving Workshop:
Using Alternative Methods

1. diameter: 4 in.; height: 6 in.
2. side length: 6 in.; height: 12 in.
3. side length: 6 in.; height: 8 in.
4. length: 19 ft; width: 6 ft; height: 2 ft

Challenge Practice

1. a.

x	−5	−4	−3	−2	−1
f(x)	−197	−109	−51	−17	−1

x	0	1	2	3	4	5
f(x)	3	1	−1	3	19	53

The polynomial is guaranteed to have a zero in $-1 \le x \le 0$, $1 \le x \le 2$, and $2 \le x \le 3$.

b.

x	−5	−4	−3	−2	−1
f(x)	1372	509	132	13	−4

x	0	1	2	3	4	5
f(x)	−3	4	77	348	1021	2372

The polynomial is guaranteed to have a zero in $-2 \le x \le -1$ and $0 \le x \le 1$.

c.

x	−5	−4	−3	−2	−1
f(x)	−2310	−1287	−616	−225	−42

x	0	1	2	3	4	5
f(x)	5	−12	−21	50	273	720

The polynomial is guaranteed to have a zero in $-1 \le x \le 0$, $0 \le x \le 1$, and $2 \le x \le 3$.

d.

x	−5	−4	−3	−2	−1
f(x)	826	289	64	1	−2

x	0	1	2	3	4	5
f(x)	1	4	49	226	673	1576

The polynomial is guaranteed to have a zero in $-2 \le x \le -1$ and $-1 \le x \le 0$.

2. a. The possible rational zeros are ± 1. Neither of these values are actual zeros of the function because when the function is evaluated at $x = -1$ and $x = 1$, you do not obtain 0.

b.

x	−5	−4	−3	−2	−1
f(x)	−99	−47	−17	−3	1

x	0	1	2	3	4	5
f(x)	1	3	13	37	81	151

The polynomial is guaranteed to have a zero in $-2 \le x \le -1$.

Lesson 5.6, continued

c.

x	-2	-1.9	-1.8	-1.7	-1.6
$f(x)$	-3	-2.249	-1.592	-1.023	-0.536

x	-1.5	-1.4	-1.3	-1.2	-1.1	-1
$f(x)$	-0.125	0.216	0.493	0.712	0.879	1

The polynomial is guaranteed to have a zero in $-1.5 \le x \le -1.4$.

d. The zero approximated to three decimal points is -1.446.

3. The optimal order size is between 4000 and 5000 units.

Lesson 5.7

Teaching Guide

1. If $f(x) = a_n x^n + \cdots + a_1 x + a_0$ has integer coefficients, then every rational zero of f has the following form: $\dfrac{p}{q} = \dfrac{\text{factor of constant term } a_0}{\text{factor of leading coefficient } a_n}$.

2. $\pm 1, \pm 2, \pm 4, \pm 8, \pm 16, \pm \dfrac{1}{2}$

3. $\dfrac{-b \pm \sqrt{b^2 - 4ac}}{2a}$; two imaginary solutions

4. two complex numbers of the form $a + bi$ and $a - bi$; 31

Investigating Algebra Activity

1. a. 2, 2 **b.** 3, 3 **c.** 4, 4 **2.** They are the same.

3. *Sample answer:* The degree of a polynomial indicates how many zeros, or solutions, the polynomial will have. For example, $x^5 - 3x^2 + 32$ is a polynomial of degree 5, so it will have 5 solutions.

Practice Level A

1. 2 **2.** 3 **3.** 3 **4.** 4 **5.** 5 **6.** 4 **7.** 1 **8.** 3
9. $3 + \sqrt{2}$ **10.** $-i$ **11.** $-2 + 9i$ **12.** $\sqrt{3} + i$
13. $1 - i\sqrt{5}$ **14.** $\sqrt{2} - i\sqrt{7}$ **15.** $-3, 2, 9$
16. $-4, 1, 5$ **17.** $-6, -i, i$ **18.** $-8, -\sqrt{7}, \sqrt{7}$
19. $2, -3i, 3i$ **20.** $-\sqrt{5}, \sqrt{5}, -2i, 2i$
21. $f(x) = x + 9$ **22.** $f(x) = x^2 + x - 20$
23. $f(x) = x^2 + 4x + 3$ **24.** $f(x) = x^3 - x$
25. $f(x) = x^3 - 7x^2 + 4x + 12$
26. $f(x) = x^3 - 7x^2 - 28x - 20$

27. 2 real zeros; no imaginary zeros
28. about 0.28 in. or about 3.70 in.

Practice Level B

1. 3 **2.** 6 **3.** 7 **4.** 5 **5.** $-1, 1, 3$
6. $-4, 0, 2, 6$ **7.** $-5, -i, i$ **8.** $2, 7, -3i, 3i$
9. $-3, 2 + \sqrt{3}, 2 - \sqrt{3}$ **10.** $-1, \dfrac{1}{2}, -i, i$

11. $f(x) = x^2 + 11x + 28$
12. $f(x) = x^3 - 8x^2 + 17x - 10$
13. $f(x) = x^3 + 2x^2 - 3x$
14. $f(x) = x^3 - 4x^2 + x - 4$
15. $f(x) = x^4 + 5x^3 + 4x^2 + 20x$
16. $f(x) = x^3 - 12x^2 + 37x - 40$ **17.** D
18. $-2.09, 0.57, 2.51$ **19.** $-0.62, -0.50, 1.62$
20. $-0.47, 1.40$ **21.** $-4.09, -0.98, 1.47, 4.60$
22. 2002 **23.** 3 and 9 years after opening

Practice Level C

1. $-3, -1, 3$ **2.** $-1, 1, 2 + \sqrt{3}, 2 - \sqrt{3}$
3. $-2, 0, 2 + i\sqrt{3}, 2 - i\sqrt{3}$ **4.** $-4, -2, \dfrac{5}{2}, 4$
5. $-3, -1, 3, \dfrac{9}{2}$ **6.** $1, \dfrac{-3 \pm i\sqrt{19}}{2}$
7. $-i, i, -1 + \sqrt{2}, -1 - \sqrt{2}$ **8.** $1 + 4i, 1 - 4i,$ $\sqrt{3}, -\sqrt{3}$ **9.** $f(x) = 2x^4 - 4x^3 - 32x^2 + 64x$
10. $f(x) = 2x^4 + 58x^2 + 200$
11. $f(x) = 2x^3 + 10x^2 - 6x - 30$
12. $f(x) = 2x^3 - 12x^2 + 50x$
13. $f(x) = 2x^4 - 22x^3 + 80x^2 - 116x + 56$
14. $f(x) = 2x^6 - 26x^5 + 120x^4 - 200x^3 +$ $118x^2 - 174x$ **15.** 2 or 0; 1; 2 or 0 **16.** 2 or 0; 0; 4, 2, or 0 **17.** 4, 2, or 0; 1; 4, 2, or 0
18. 5, 3, or 1; 5, 3, or 1; 8, 6, 4, 2, or 0
19. 3 or 1; 3 or 1; 2 or 0 **20.** $-0.75, 0.75$
21. -0.86 **22.** $-1.06, 3.98$
23. $-3.65, 0, 3.11$
24. *Sample answer:* One zero is a repeated zero.;

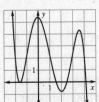

25. *Sample answer:* $f(x) = x^3 - 3x^2 - 18x + 40$ and $g(x) = 2x^3 - 6x^2 - 36x + 80$

26. a. $R = -315t^5 + 5554t^4 + 1932t^3 - 709{,}619t^2 + 6{,}441{,}145t + 49{,}246{,}365$ **b.** 2001

Study Guide

1. $1, \dfrac{1 \pm i\sqrt{7}}{2}$ **2.** $-1, 3, 1 \pm i\sqrt{3}$

3. $x^3 + 2x^2 - x - 2$ **4.** $x^3 - 5x^2 + 5x + 3$

5. $x^3 - 4x^2 + x - 4$

6. $x^4 - 4x^3 + 2x^2 - 4x + 1$ **7.** positive: 1, negative: 2 or 0, imaginary: 0 or 2 **8.** positive: 1 or 3, negative: 1, imaginary: 2 or 0

Real-Life Application

1.

t	0	1	2	3	4
S	5267	5284	5346	5455	5605

t	5	6	7	8	9
S	5784	5974	6159	6324	6455

t	10	11	12	13
S	6548	6605	6643	6689

1995

2.

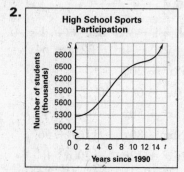

High School Sports Participation

3. $0.021t^5 - 0.572t^4 + 3.3t^3 + 16.173t^2 - 1.674t + 5267 = 6000$; $0.021t^5 - 0.572t^4 + 3.3t^3 + 16.173t^2 - 1.674t - 733 = 0$; $t \approx 6$

4. $0.021t^5 - 0.572t^4 + 3.3t^3 + 16.173t^2 - 1.674t + 5267 = 6600$; $0.021t^5 - 0.572t^4 + 3.3t^3 + 16.173t^2 - 1.674t - 1333 = 0$; $t \approx 11$

5. 2008; 2010 **6.** about 7.3 million students

Challenge Practice

1. True. For example, the function $f(x) = x^2 - 3$ has two real zeros $\pm\sqrt{3}$.

2. True. The polynomial is said to have three real zeros and one of them is rational. Then the other two real zeros must be irrational because irrational numbers are real numbers.

3. False. A cubic polynomial function must have three zeros according to the fundamental theorem of algebra. According to the complex conjugates theorem, if $a + bi$ is an imaginary zero, then $a - bi$ is also an imaginary zero. So, a cubic polynomial function can have at most two imaginary zeros and the third zero must be real.

4. False. According to the irrational conjugates theorem, if $a + \sqrt{b}$ is an irrational zero of a polynomial function, then $a - \sqrt{b}$ is also an irrational zero of the function. So, if a fourth-degree polynomial function has three rational zeros, the fourth must also be rational.

5. $f(x) = -x^3 + 2x^2 - 16x + 32$

6. $f(x) = \dfrac{1}{2}x^3 - \dfrac{1}{2}x^2 + 4x + 5$

7. $f(x) = -\dfrac{1}{3}x^4 + \dfrac{4}{3}x^3 + \dfrac{16}{3}x^2 - 8x$

8. $f(x) = 2x^3 - 30x + 8$

9. a.

Function	Zeros	Sum of zeros	Product of zeros
$f_1(x)$	$-3, 4$	1	-12
$f_2(x)$	$-6, 2, 4$	0	-48
$f_3(x)$	$-2, -1, \pm 3i$	-3	18
$f_4(x)$	$-1, 0, 4, \pm\sqrt{2}$	3	0

b. The sum of the zeros of an nth-degree polynomial is equal to the opposite of the coefficient of the x^{n-1} term. **c.** The product of the zeros of an nth-degree polynomial is equal to the constant term if the function is of even degree and to the opposite of the constant term if the function is of odd degree. **10.** The concentration is the greatest after about 4.5 hours.

Lesson 5.8

Teaching Guide

1. $(0, 3)$ and $(2, -1)$ **2.** $(1, -9)$

3. $(-1.7, 10.4)$ and $(1.7, -10.4)$

Graphing Calculator Activity

1. local maximum: $(0.37, 13.51)$; local minima: $(-1.83, -12.66)$, $(2.96, -27.04)$

2. local maximum: $(-2.54, 0.88)$; local
minimum: $(-0.13, -6.06)$ **3.** local maximum:
$(0, 36)$; local minima: $(-2.55, -6.25)$,
$(2.55, -6.25)$ **4.** local maximum $(-2.67, 29.63)$;
local minimum: $(2.0, -72)$ **5.** local maxima:
$(-1.57, 1.92)$, $(2.25, 8.63)$; local minimum:
$(0.07, -4.02)$ **6.** local maximum: $(-4.19, 16.16)$;
local minimum: $(2.86, -54.08)$

Practice Level A

1. False. *Sample answer:* If k is an imaginary
zero, then it is not an x-intercept of the graph of
$f(x)$. **2.** 4 **3.** 5 **4.** 3 **5.** $(-1.5, 5.5)$: max,
$(0.5, 3)$: min **6.** $(1, 2)$: min **7.** $(-1.5, -3.75)$:
min, $(0.5, 1.25)$: max, $(1, 1)$: min **8.** B **9.** C

10. A **11.** $(-4, 0), (1, 0)$ **12.** $(2, 0), (3, 0)$

13. $(-4, 0), (0, 0), (5, 0)$ **14.** $(-3, 0), (-1, 0)$,
$(8, 0)$ **15.** $(-6, 0)$ **16.** $(1, 0), (7, 0)$

17. 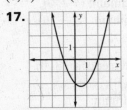 **18.**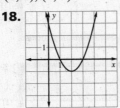

19. 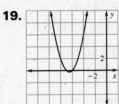 **20.**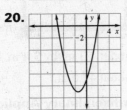

21. 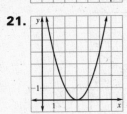 **22.**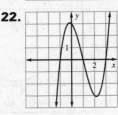

23. a. 4 **b.** 4 **c.** $(-2, 0), (6, 0)$ **24. a.** $0 < x < 9$,
because the sides must be less than 9 inches.
b. 3 in. **c.** 432 in.^{3}

Practice Level B

1. The error is in calling -6 a factor. The correct
statement is *If -6 is a solution of the polynomial
equation $f(x) = 0$, then $(x + 6)$ is a factor of $f(x)$.*

2. 3 **3.** 2 **4.** 5 **5.** 1 **6.** 6 **7.** 8 **8.** $-3, 2, 5$

9. $-4, 6, 8$ **10.** $-3, 2$ **11.** $-5, -1, 7$

12. $-6, -2$ **13.** 8

14. 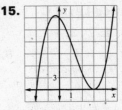 **15.**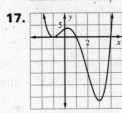

16. 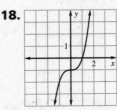 **17.**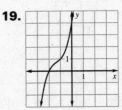

18. 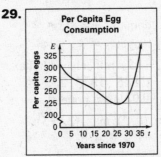 **19.**

20. $(-0.5, 0.5)$: max, $(0.5, -0.3)$: min; $-0.9, 0$,
0.6; 3 **21.** $(-2, 0)$: min, $(-0.5, 5)$: max, $(1, 0)$:
min; $-2, 1$; 4 **22.** $(-2.8, 1.9)$: max, $(0, 0.25)$:
min, $(2, 1)$: max; $-3.8, 2.8$; 4 **23.** x-int: -1.79,
$0.11, 1.67$; max: $(-1, 7)$; min: $(1, -5)$

24. x-int: $-2, 1$; max: $(1, 0)$; min: $\left(-1, -\frac{4}{3}\right)$

25. x-int: $-2.83, 0, 2.83$; max: $(-2, 4), (2, 4)$;
min: $(0, 0)$ **26.** x-int: $-1.73, 0, 1.73$; max:
$(-1.73, 0), (0.77, 4.46)$; min: $(-0.77, -4.46)$,
$(1.73, 0)$ **27.** x-int: $-2, -1, 0, 1, 2$; max:
$(-1.64, 3.63), (0.54, 1.42)$; min: $(-0.54, -1.42)$,
$(1.64, -3.63)$ **28.** x-int: $-1.53, -0.35, 1.88, 2$;
max: $(0.61, 3.62)$; min: $(-1.05, -3.03)$,
$(1.94, -0.03)$

29.

$(25.33, 222.93)$; *Sample answer:* From 1970 to
1995, per capita egg consumption decreased to
about 223 eggs, then began to increase again.

30. a. $\ell = \dfrac{600}{\pi r} - r$ **b.** $V = 300r - 0.5\pi r^3$

c. 1596 ft^3; $r \approx 7.98$ ft, $\ell \approx 15.95$ ft

Lesson 5.8, continued

Practice Level C

1. 3 **2.** 2 **3.** 4

4.

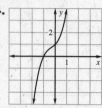

domain: $-\infty < x < \infty$
range: $-\infty < y < \infty$

5.

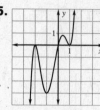

domain: $-\infty < x < \infty$
range: $-\infty < y < \infty$

6.

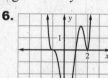

domain: $-\infty < x < \infty$
range: $y \geq -4.489$

7.

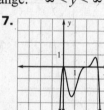

domain: $-\infty < x < \infty$
range: $y \leq 0.8$

8.

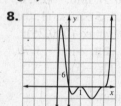

domain: $-\infty < x < \infty$
range: $-\infty < y < \infty$

9.

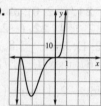

domain: $-\infty < x < \infty$
range: $-\infty < y < \infty$

10.

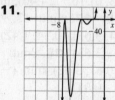

domain: $-\infty < x < \infty$
range: $y \geq -22.9$

11.

domain: $-\infty < x < \infty$
range: $-\infty < y < \infty$

12. $(-2, 2.4)$: max, $(0, -1.2)$: min, $(1, -1)$: max, $(2.4, -2)$: min; $-2.5, -1, 3; 5$ **13.** $(-2, -1)$: max, $(0, -2.2)$: min, $(1, -2)$: max; none; 4

14. $(-1.5, -2.25)$: min, $(0, 3)$: max, $(2, -3)$: min, $(3.5, 2)$: max; $-2, -1, 1, 3, 4; 5$

15. x-int: $-0.34, 1.43, 2.1$; max: $(0.7, 2.44)$; min: $(1.83, -1.55)$ **16.** x-int: $0, 1.2$; max: $(-1.19, 4.09)$; min: $(-1.77, 3.8)$, $(0.71, -2.93)$

17. x-int: $-0.88, 1.08, 1.41$; max: $(1.26, 0.08)$; min: $(0, -0.88)$ **18.** x-int: $-5, 0, 1.2$; max: $(0.42, 1.38)$; min: $(-3.57, -116.16)$, $(1.2, 0)$

19. -1 **20.** $2, 4$ **21.** $1, 3, 5$

22. If n is even, there is a turning point. If n is odd, the graph passes through the x-axis.;

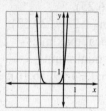

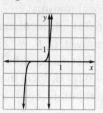

23. a. $h = \dfrac{500 - 2\pi r^2}{\pi r}$

b. $V = 500r - \dfrac{4}{3}\pi r^3$

c. about 2103 ft^3; $r \approx 6.31$ ft, $h \approx 12.6$ ft

Study Guide

1.

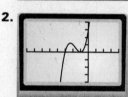

; x-intercepts: $(-2, 0)$, $(4, 0)$; maximum: $(-2, 0)$, minimum: $(2, -16)$

2.

; x-intercepts: $(-3, 0)$, $(-1, 0)$; maximum: $(-2.33, 1.19)$, minimum: $(-1, 0)$

3. about 1.3 in. by 3.4 in. by 9.4 in.

4. about 41.6 in.^3

Interdisciplinary Application

1.

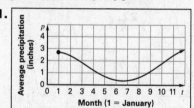

2. greatest: December; least: July **3.** about 18.66 in.

Challenge Practice

1.

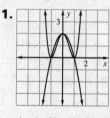

$(-1, 0), (0, 2),$
$(1, 0)$

2.

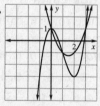

$(0, 1), (1, -1), (3, 1)$

Lesson 5.8, continued

3.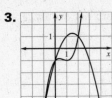

$(-1, -5), (0, -1),$
$(2, 1)$

4.

$(-1, 0), (1, 0)$

5. maximum: $(-5, 76)$; minimum: $\left(\dfrac{1}{3}, \dfrac{4}{27}\right)$

6. maximum: $(-2, 68)$; minimum: $(3, -57)$

7. maximum: $(2, 14)$; minimum: $\left(-\dfrac{2}{3}, \dfrac{122}{27}\right)$

8. maximum: $(6, 323)$; minimum: $(-1, -20)$

9. The coefficient of the x^3-term of the cubic function is three times the coefficient of the x^2-term of the quadratic equation. The coefficient of the x^2-term of the cubic function is twice the coefficient of the x-term of the quadratic equation. The coefficient of the x-term of the cubic function is the same as the constant term of the quadratic equation. **a.** $3x^2 + 18x + 24 = 0$; maximum: $(-4, -13)$; minimum: $(-2, -17)$

b. $3x^2 - 2x - 8 = 0$; maximum: $\left(-\dfrac{4}{3}, \dfrac{392}{27}\right)$; minimum: $(2, -4)$ **c.** $-6x^2 - 66x - 60 = 0$; maximum: $(-1, 41)$; minimum: $(-10, -688)$

Lesson 5.9

Teaching Guide

1 and 3.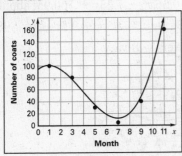

2. *Sample answer:* The data appears to go down, then up, but not at the same rate, so a cubic function would be better than a quadratic function.

Practice Level A

1. $f(x) = (x + 1)(x - 1)(x - 3)$

2. $f(x) = (x + 3)(x + 2)(x - 1)$

3. $f(x) = (x + 3)(x + 1)(x - 4)$

4. $f(x) = (x + 4)(x + 2)(x - 5)$

5. $f(x) = (x + 1)(x - 2)(x - 4)$

6. $f(x) = (x - 1)(x - 2)(x - 3)$

7. $f(x) = (x + 3)(x + 4)(x + 5)$

8.

$f(1)$	$f(2)$	$f(3)$	$f(4)$	$f(5)$	$f(6)$	$f(7)$
-1	6	15	26	39	54	71

7   9   11   13   15   17

2   2   2   2   2

9.

$f(1)$	$f(2)$	$f(3)$	$f(4)$	$f(5)$	$f(6)$	$f(7)$
5	7	19	47	97	175	287

2   12   28   50   78   112

10   16   22   28   34

6   6   6   6

10. 3   **11.** 2

12.

$f(1)$	$f(2)$	$f(3)$	$f(4)$	$f(5)$	$f(6)$	$f(7)$
1	6	15	28	45	66	91

5   9   13   17   21   25

4   4   4   4   4

13. a. $r = 0.0014t^3 - 0.086t^2 + 2.18t + 38$
b. 69%

Practice Level B

1. $f(x) = (x + 2)(x + 1)(x - 2)$

2. $f(x) = 2(x + 1)(x - 1)(x - 3)$

3. $f(x) = \dfrac{1}{2}(x - 2)(x - 3)(x - 4)$

4. $f(x) = \dfrac{1}{8}x(x + 2)(x - 1)$

5. $f(x) = \dfrac{1}{9}(x + 4)(x + 1)(x - 3)$

6. $f(x) = -\dfrac{1}{80}(x + 5)(x - 3)(x - 4)$

7. $f(x) = \dfrac{2}{3}x(x + 3)(x - 1)$

8.

$f(1)$	$f(2)$	$f(3)$	$f(4)$	$f(5)$	$f(6)$	$f(7)$
0	-1	-10	-33	-76	-145	-246

-1 -9 -23 -43 -69 -101

-8 -14 -20 -26 -32

-6 -6 -6 -6

9. $f(1)$ $f(2)$ $f(3)$ $f(4)$ $f(5)$ $f(6)$ $f(7)$

  −1   −21   −51   −61   3   219   689

   −20   −30   −10   64   216   470

    −10   20   74   152   254

     30   54   78   102

      24   24   24

10. $f(x) = x^3 + 2x^2 + x + 1$

11. $f(x) = x^3 − 3x^2 + x − 4$

12. a. $y = 0.007t^3 − 0.74t^2 + 49t − 236$
b. about 101 sec

Practice Level C

1. $f(x) = (x + 5)(x + 2)(x − 1)$

2. $f(x) = −2(x + 2)(x − 1)(x − 2)$

3. $f(x) = (x + 1)(x − 2)^2$

4. $f(x) = \dfrac{3}{2}(x + 1)(x − 2)(x − 3)$

5. $f(x) = \dfrac{3}{2}\left(x + \dfrac{1}{2}\right)(x − 1)(x − 3)$

6. $f(x) = −8\left(x − \dfrac{1}{2}\right)\left(x − \dfrac{3}{2}\right)(x − 3)$

7. $f(x) = 12\left(x + \dfrac{1}{3}\right)\left(x − \dfrac{1}{4}\right)(x − 1)$

8. $f(1)$ $f(2)$ $f(3)$ $f(4)$ $f(5)$ $f(6)$ $f(7)$

  −4   −12   −6   56   240   636   1358

   −8   6   62   184   396   722

    14   56   122   212   326

     42   66   90   114

      24   24   24

9. $f(1)$ $f(2)$ $f(3)$ $f(4)$ $f(5)$ $f(6)$ $f(7)$

  5   18   55   128   249   430   683

   13   37   73   121   181   253

    24   36   48   60   72

     12   12   12   12

10. $f(x) = x^3 + 8x^2 − 12x + 13$

11. $f(x) = x^3 − 10x^2 + 8x − 15$

12. a. $y = −0.0638t^3 + 1.073t^2 + 12.13t + 489$

b. about \$694 **c.** The *t*-values are not evenly spaced.

Study Guide

1. $y = −(x + 2)(x − 4)(x − 1)$

2. $y = (x + 3)(x + 5)(x − 2)$

3. $f(1)$ $f(2)$ $f(3)$ $f(4)$

  3   11   24   42

   8   13   18

    5   5

4. $y = −2x^2 + 14x − 12$

Problem Solving Workshop: Mixed Problem Solving

1. a. $x^3 + 7x^2 + 12x − 360 = 0$ **b.** ±1, ±2, ±3, ±4, ±5, ±6, ±8, ±10, ±12, ±15, ±20, ±24, ±30, ±40, ±60, ±120 **c.** 5; After factoring the equation, you have $(x − 5)(x^2 + 12x + 72)$. The second factor has no zero. **d.** The base is 5 in. by 8 in. and the height is 9 in.

2. a. $V = 4x^3 − 56x^2 + 187x$

b.

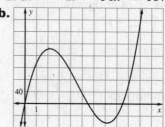

c. 12.6 in. by 6.6 in. by 2.2 in. **d.** about 183 in.^{3}

3. $c = 0.36x^2 + 7.23x + 160.95$; about \$284,000

4. 1995 **5.** $p = 2.5t^2 − 9.5t + 14$; \$98

6. Answers will vary.

7. a.

b. $V = \dfrac{1}{3}\pi x^2(x + 3)$

c.

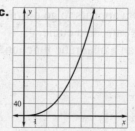

about 6

Lesson 5.9, continued

d. $\frac{1}{3}\pi x^2(x + 3) = 108\pi$; $x = 6$; The answer is the same as the estimate. The candle has a radius of 6 in. and a height of 9 in.

Challenge Practice

1. $f(x) = \frac{1}{2}(x^4 - 15x^2 + 10x + 24)$

2. $f(x) = \frac{1}{4}(2x^4 + x^3 - 98x^2 - 289x - 120)$

3. $f(x) = -\frac{1}{2}(2x^5 + 5x^4 - 11x^3 - 20x^2 + 12x)$

4. $f(x) = \frac{1}{4}(x^5 - x^4 - 27x^3 + 41x^2 + 106x - 120)$

5. a. fourth-order differences for normal monthly high temperatures: $-1, 0, -1, 3, 2, 1, 1, 0$; fourth-order differences for normal monthly low temperatures: $-1, 0, 1, 0, 4, -3, 5, -1$; The fourth-order differences are not all equal, but they are close. So, a quartic function can be used to model both sets of data.

b. $H = 0.04724t^4 - 1.364t^3 + 11.68t^2 - 26.4t + 46$; $L = 0.03864t^4 - 1.139t^3 + 10.037t^2 - 24.2t + 35$

c.

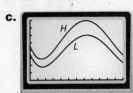

d. For the model given by H, the local maximum occurs at approximately (7.2, 79.3) which means the monthly normal high temperature is greatest in July with a temperature of 79.3°F. The local minimum occurs at approximately (1.5, 28.3) which means the monthly normal high temperature is least in the middle of January with a temperature of 28.3°F. For the model given by L, the local maximum occurs at approximately (7.4, 59.9) which means the monthly normal low temperature is greatest in July with a temperature of 59.9°F. The local minimum occurs at approximately (1.6, 17.6) which means the monthly normal low temperature is least in the middle of January with a temperature of 17.6°F.

e. The difference between the normal high and low temperatures is greatest during the summer months and smallest during the winter months.

f. June 21 is represented by about $t = 6.7$. This does not agree with the maximum values from part (d). There is about 1 month of lag time.

Review and Project

Review Games and Activities

1. $\frac{9y^6}{4x^9}$ **2.** $f(x) = -15$ **3.** $3x^3 - 4x^2 + 4x - 5$

4. $x^3 + x^2 - 17x + 15$ **5.** $3x^2(x + 4)(x - 1)$

6. $x = 3, 1, 0, -1, -3$

7. $4x^2 - 3x - 22 + \dfrac{21x + 120}{x^2 + 5}$

8. $3, 2, -5$

GEOMETRY

Project: Playing the Game

1. *Sample answer:* Questions related to polynomial functions are written on index cards. Each question is rated 1 to 6, with 6 being the most difficult. Players take turns rolling a number cube and choosing a question with the appropriate rating. If the player answers the question correctly, the player receives the number of points shown on the number cube. The first player to receive 40 points wins. **2.** Check students' work. Questions can be either specific problems related to a given polynomial (e.g. solve an equation or factor a polynomial), or they may be conceptual questions. Students could create a game where polynomials are used to generate numbers in the game, such as evaluating a polynomial to determine how many moves to take in a board game. **3.** Check students' work. **4.** Check students' work.

Cumulative Review

1. 15 mi/h **2.** 27.5 m/sec **3.** 8 **4.** 1 **5.** 1

6. $x > -3$;

7. $x \le 1$;

8. 15 **9.** $\frac{3}{2}$, 0 **10.** parallel **11.** parallel

12. x-intercept: $\frac{5}{2}$, y-intercept: $-\frac{5}{3}$

13. x-intercept: $\frac{1}{3}$, y-intercept: -1

14. x-intercept: -2, y-intercept: -4

Review and Project, continued

15. $y = -\frac{5}{2}x$ **16.** $y = -4x$

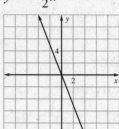 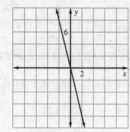

17. 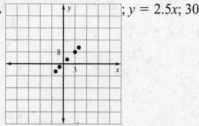 ; $y = 2.5x$; 30

18. no, yes   **19.** yes, no   **20.** 20 one dollar bills, 5 five dollar bills   **21.** $(2, 1)$ **22.** $(-2, 3)$

23. $(-1, 0, 2)$ **24.** $x = 1, y = 1$

25. $x = 2, y = 3$ **26.** $\begin{bmatrix} 6 & -2 \\ 0 & -5 \end{bmatrix}$ **27.** $\begin{bmatrix} -5 \\ 22 \end{bmatrix}$

28. 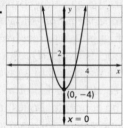 ; vertex: $(0, -4)$, axis of symmetry: $x = 0$

29. 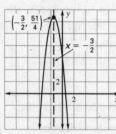 ; vertex: $-\left(\frac{3}{2}, \frac{51}{4}\right)$, axis of symmetry: $x = -\frac{3}{2}$

30. 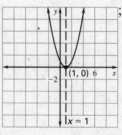 ; vertex: $(1, 0)$, axis of symmetry: $x = 1$

31. 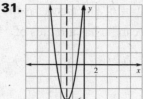 ; vertex: $(-3, -6)$, axis of symmetry: $x = -3$

32. $(g - 1)(g - 2)$ **33.** cannot be factored

34. cannot be factored   **35.** $(2q - 3)(q - 1)$

36. $\frac{3 \pm \sqrt{33}}{2}$ **37.** $\frac{-1 \pm \sqrt{15}}{2}$ **38.** $-1, 5$

39. 2^8, product of powers

40. 4^3, quotient of powers

41. 3^6, power of a power   **42.** 23   **43.** -2

44. $(x - 2)^2(x - 1)$ **45.** $(x - 2)(x^2 + 2x + 4)$

46. $(2x^2 - 5)(x + 3)$ **47.** $-\frac{3}{2}$ **48.** $1, 1, -7$

49. 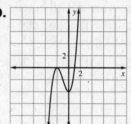   **50.**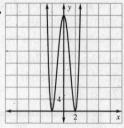

51. $f(x) = x^3 + x^2 - 2x$
52. $f(x) = x^3 - 2x^2 + x + 2$

Algebra 2
Chapter 5 Resource Book

A18